Spelling
High School
Workbook

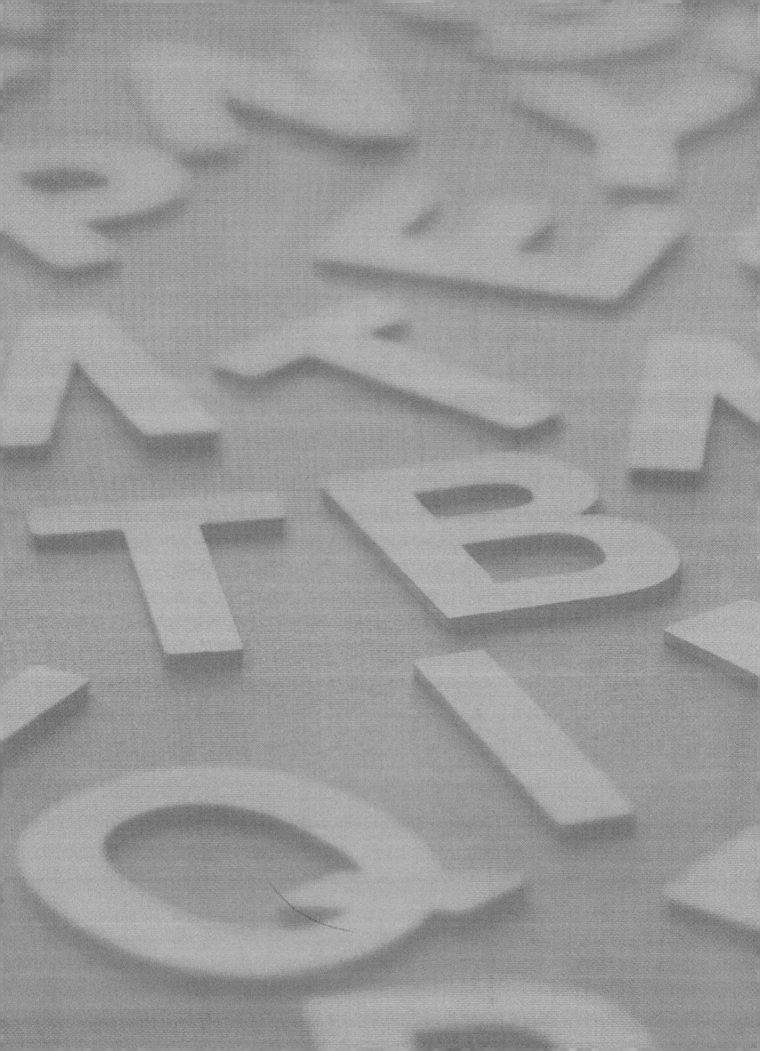

Spelling

High School

Workbook

Grades 9-10

Vocabulary and Writing Practice
with Interactive Activities

Natasha Attard Ph.D

Printed in the USA

ISBN Paperback 978-9918-9583-7-5

To my boys, Giovanni and Beppe, with much love.

Also by Natasha Attard, Ph.D.

The Spelling Practice Workbook 6th Grade: Guided Activities to Increase your Word Power. Consolidates and Complements Homeschooling of the English Language

The Spelling Practice Workbook 7th Grade: Guided Activities to Increase your Word Power. Consolidates and Complements Homeschooling of the English Language

The Spelling Practice Workbook 8th Grade: Guided Activities to Increase your Word Power. Consolidates and Complements Homeschooling of the English Language

Vocabulary and Spelling Practice 7th Grade: Intensive Practice Workbook and Guided Activities to Increase Your Word Power.

Vocabulary Building 7th Grade Workbook: Guided Activities to Increase your Word Power. Consolidates and Complements Homeschooling of the English Language

Table of Contents

Author's Message

**Thank you for purchasing
"Spelling High School Workbook Grades 9-10"**

Welcome to a journey that will not only enhance your spelling skills but also deepen your understanding of how words function within the English language. My teaching philosophy is grounded in the belief that the best way to master spelling and word usage is through extensive practice across a variety of contexts. This workbook is designed to provide you with just that—a range of engaging activities that include reading, drilling, writing, and interactive online games.

Have you ever felt amazed and empowered when you could effortlessly understand complex texts and grasp the academic vocabulary within? Such a level of word knowledge eliminates the frustration of stumbling over unfamiliar terms, particularly those crucial for comprehending sophisticated ideas. Whether it's understanding a complex scientific concept, an intricate argument, or a multi-dimensional character in literature, this book is here to guide you.

This is not just a spelling workbook. Consider spelling and word knowledge as intricately connected like the threads of a spider's web—each word supports and enhances the understanding of others. Here, you will practice not only the spelling of complex and challenging words but also their application in diverse contexts. Through sentences, lengthy passages, and comprehensive definitions provided for reference, you will see these words come alive. Moreover, you'll engage actively with these terms in various writing exercises.

The vocabulary selected for this workbook falls into Tier 2 academic vocabulary—words that you will frequently encounter in complex texts across different subjects. By presenting these words within context, the workbook is designed to help you decipher their meanings and uses from the surrounding text, enhancing your ability to understand and apply them in your writing. Each lesson is structured to introduce you to 8 to 12 new words. You'll learn how to spell these words and use them effectively in sentences and broader contexts:

- **Word Usage and Spelling Practice:** You will start with passages and sentences that showcase the target words in different contexts, accompanied by definitions to build a solid foundational understanding. Subsequent spelling drills will reinforce this knowledge, breaking down each word into syllables and then piecing them back together.
- **Application and Writing Integration:** This section challenges you to use your new vocabulary in various writing activities, including prompts and comprehension passages that encourage deeper engagement with each word.
- **Interactive Online Games:** Enjoy a selection of interactive online games and quizzes—from escape rooms to adventures in ancient Egypt—that make learning both fun and effective. These games reinforce the spelling and meanings of the words you've learned.
- **Extended Writing Practice:** As you progress, the tasks will invite you to compose longer texts, utilizing the vocabulary in ways that cement your learning and enhance your writing skills.
- **Self-reflection and Goal-setting Pages:** Each lesson includes a self-reflection page to help you assess your confidence in both spelling and usage of the vocabulary, along with a goal-setting page. Here, you will plan your approach to the new words of the upcoming lesson.
- **Final Test:** Upon completing the workbook, you are invited to evaluate your mastery of the spelling and word knowledge covered by taking a final online test. The password needed to access this test is provided within the workbook. The test comprises 25 multiple-choice questions focusing on both spelling accuracy and word usage. After submitting the test, you will promptly receive a score report, detailing which answers were correct and which were incorrect. This feedback will help you gauge your progress and solidify your understanding of the material.
- **Answer Key:** An answer key is provided for all word usage activities within this workbook, including suggested responses to writing prompts. This resource is designed to support your learning by offering possible solutions, allowing you to compare your answers and deepen your understanding of how vocabulary can be effectively applied in various contexts.
- **Word Glossary:** In the final section of this workbook, you'll find a comprehensive list of all the words covered throughout the lessons, along with their definitions. This mini-dictionary of Tier 2 academic vocabulary offers a handy reference to reinforce your study.

By the end of this workbook, my ultimate aim is for you to be able to confidently write and use these words correctly in the appropriate contexts. Mastering this vocabulary will equip you for standardized tests such as the SAT, ACT, and AP exams, where a strong command of sophisticated and well-written vocabulary can significantly impact your scores. This workbook prepares you not just for academic success in high school but also sets a solid foundation for your future educational endeavors.

Thank you for choosing this workbook. I am excited to be a part of your academic growth and look forward to seeing how far you will go.

How to Use this Book

Teachers and parents can use this workbook as a standalone resource. The vocabulary selected for this workbook comprises Tier 2 Academic Vocabulary. These words are particularly emphasized across high school curricula due to their frequent appearance in complex texts across various disciplines. Tier 2 words are pivotal for academic success because they are commonly used in written and oral communication within academic settings but are less likely to be acquired through everyday spoken language.

This workbook has 20 lessons divided into sections. Designed with a general progression in mind, the activities within each lesson gradually increase in challenge to build and expand the student's vocabulary and spelling skills. However, recognizing the importance of differentiated learning, the workbook is structured to intersperse less challenging activities throughout each lesson. This approach allows students of varying abilities to engage successfully at their own pace, providing multiple entry points to the learning process. By progressively building on previous knowledge and varying the difficulty within each lesson, the workbook caters to a diverse range of learning styles and needs.

Lesson Sections

As you guide students through the workbook, here are the various structured activities they will encounter:

- **Word Usage and Spelling Practice:** Students begin with exposure to new vocabulary, learning its usage through context-rich passages and its structure through detailed spelling and syllabification.
- **Application and Writing Integration:** This section is designed to engage students in spelling and applying their newly acquired vocabulary through a variety of writing tasks. By practicing the spelling while also using these words in extended writing exercises, students reinforce their understanding and retention of both the spelling and the meanings of the words. This dual-focus approach not only helps students express their ideas clearly but also deepens their grasp of how to use the vocabulary contextually.

- **Interactive Online Games and Quizzes:** This workbook features eight interactive games focusing on spelling and word usage, placed after every two or three lessons to reinforce and assess students' learning. These games allow students to apply their knowledge in a dynamic setting, enhancing vocabulary retention and enabling both students and educators to monitor progress effectively.
- **Extended Writing Practice:** This section is introduced in later lessons and focuses on providing more practice with students' spelling and word usage through diverse writing exercises. As students' skills evolve, they will encounter increasingly complex writing assignments that require precise articulation of concepts and arguments, further reinforcing their mastery of vocabulary and proper spelling.
- **Self-reflection and Goal-setting:** Each lesson concludes with a reflection and goal-setting phase, designed to encourage students to monitor their own progress and hold themselves accountable for their learning journey. This process is crucial for students to assess their understanding and set objectives for future lessons. It also provides teachers and parents with valuable insights into each student's progress, allowing them to offer targeted support where needed.

Final Test

At the conclusion of the workbook, students are required to take an online final test designed to assess their mastery of the vocabulary covered throughout the lessons. This test consists of multiple-choice questions that evaluate both spelling accuracy and correct usage of words in context. Students will find the password needed to access the test included in the workbook. At the start of the test, students must enter their email address. Upon completion, they will then receive an immediate score report, which provides a detailed analysis of their performance. This feedback will assist them in assessing their progress and reinforcing the learning objectives of the workbook.

Answer Key

An answer key is included for all word usage activities in this workbook, which provides suggested responses to writing prompts and other exercises. This resource is particularly useful for guiding discussions and providing feedback, helping to ensure that students fully grasp and effectively apply the vocabulary in various contexts.

Word Glossary

In the final section of this workbook, a comprehensive list of all the words covered throughout the lessons, along with their definitions, is provided, offering a handy reference for review and study.

Common Core State Standards

This workbook is designed to align with the following Common Core State Standards for English Language Arts, ensuring that the activities and exercises support the curriculum requirements for grades 9-10:

CCSS.ELA-LITERACY.L.9-10.4
Determine or clarify the meaning of unknown and multiple-meaning words and phrases based on grades 9–10 reading and content, choosing flexibly from a range of strategies.

CCSS.ELA-LITERACY.L.9-10.5
Demonstrate understanding of figurative language, word relationships, and nuances in word meanings.

CCSS.ELA-LITERACY.L.9-10.6
Acquire and use accurately general academic and domain-specific words and phrases, sufficient for reading, writing, speaking, and listening at the college and career readiness level.

CCSS.ELA-LITERACY.W.9-10.4
Produce clear and coherent writing in which the development, organization, and style are appropriate to task, purpose, and audience.

CCSS.ELA-LITERACY.W.9-10.5
Develop and strengthen writing as needed by planning, revising, editing, rewriting, or trying a new approach, focusing on addressing what is most significant for a specific purpose and audience.

CCSS.ELA-LITERACY.W.9-10.10
Write routinely over extended time frames (time for research, reflection, and revision) and shorter time frames (a single sitting or a day or two) for a range of tasks, purposes, and audiences.

Lesson 1

In this part of your workbook, we focus on how words work. You'll find a list of targeted words along with their definitions presented in a box, typically on the right-hand side or in the middle of the page. These words are featured in various contexts—whether it's short excerpts, full paragraphs, or single sentences—to help you grasp how they are actually used in real life.

Now, let's go over how to make the most of this section.

1. Read with Purpose:
    a. **Pause at Each Target Word:** Whenever you encounter a target word in the text, stop.
    b. **Check the Definition:** Take a moment to read its definition from the box. This helps integrate the word's meaning with how it's used in the passage.
    c. **Continue:** After checking the definition, continue reading until you find the next target word and repeat the process.

2. Spot New Words: Notice any unfamiliar words not listed as target words? Write them down in the space provided! You can add these to your personal practice list.

3. Break It Down:
    a. **Syllabification Drill:** Next, we'll break the target words into syllables. This exercise is crucial for understanding how words are constructed, which aids in spelling and pronunciation.
    b. **Full Drill:** Finally, you'll complete a comprehensive drill to cement your understanding and recall of these words.

Why Context Matters: Learning words in context, rather than isolated spelling drills, shows you how they function in actual communication. This method not only helps you remember their meanings but also improves your ability to use them confidently in your own writing and speaking.

Ready to boost your spelling and vocabulary? Let's get started!

Remember: Read with purpose
- pause at each target word,
- review its definition, and then
- continue.

Precision in Scientific Discoveries

In the realm of scientific discovery, the presentation of findings must be **accurate** to ensure that conclusions drawn are **reliable** and can contribute to the broader field of knowledge. Researchers often arrange their data in **chronological** order, which helps to provide **context** for their experiments and observations, illustrating how results evolved over time. This methodical approach allows them to **convey** the significance of their work clearly and effectively to both the scientific community and the public. Through such **rigorously** structured communication, science becomes **accessible**, enabling us to navigate the complexities of the natural world with greater understanding.

Target Word Definitions

Accurate: Free from errors or mistakes.

Reliable: Can be depended upon for consistency and trustworthiness.

Chronological: Events arranged in the order of time they occurred.

Context: The circumstances surrounding an event or an idea, that help explain its meaning.

Convey: To communicate or express something, with or without using words.

Rigorous (rigorously): Defines something that involves strict adherence to standards and attention to detail.

Accessible: Easy to reach, enter or to understand.

List any other words from the passage you want to practice for meaning or spelling.

Spelling	Definition
Inaccurate	_____
_____	_____
_____	_____
_____	_____

Breaking down words into syllables helps you understand the structure and rhythm of words, making spelling easier and more accurate. Notice any tricky letter positions while practicing.

Accurate	ac - cu - rate	accurate	accurate
Reliable	re - li - a - ble	reliable	reliable
Chronological	chron - o - log - i - cal	Chronological	Chronological
Context	con - text	context	contex
Convey	con - vey	convey	convey
Rigorous	rig - or - ous	rigorous	rigorous
Accessible	ac - ces - si - ble	accessible	accessible

Now write each word in full.

Accurate	accurate	accurate	accurate
Reliable	reliable	reliabe	reliabe
Chronological	Chronological	Chronological	chronological
Context	Context	context	Context
Convey	convey	convey	Convey
Rigorous	rigorous	rigorous	rigorous
Accessible	accessible	accessible	accessible

My List of Words

_____   _____   _____

_____   _____   _____

_____   _____   _____

_____   _____   _____

Read the following letter and then answer the questions that follow.

The Discovery of Atlantis

Date: March 15, 1923

To Whom It May Concern,

I, Dr. Theodore Westfield, renowned archaeologist and explorer, hereby document the astonishing discovery of the legendary lost city of Atlantis. This remarkable find occurred during an expedition funded by the Royal Society for Antiquities, conducted in the waters of the Atlantic Ocean off the coast of Portugal.

Upon diving to depths previously unexplored by modern science, my team and I stumbled upon the remnants of an ancient civilization hidden beneath the ocean's surface. The structures we encountered were of a sophistication and grandeur unparalleled in any known human civilization, leading us to believe that we had indeed discovered the fabled city of Atlantis, as described by the philosopher Plato.

The artifacts recovered from the site provide tantalizing glimpses into the culture and technology of this enigmatic civilization. Among the finds are intricately carved statues depicting mythical creatures, ornate pottery adorned with elaborate designs, and fragments of inscribed tablets bearing cryptic symbols and hieroglyphs.

Our initial analysis suggests that Atlantis flourished during the Bronze Age, with a level of advancement surpassing that of contemporary civilizations. However, further study and excavation will be necessary to unravel the full extent of Atlantis's history and significance.
In light of this groundbreaking discovery, I urge scholars and historians to approach the study of Atlantis with the utmost rigor and scholarly integrity. It is imperative that we examine the evidence with an open mind and a critical eye, seeking to convey our findings accurately and responsibly to the wider world.

In conclusion, the discovery of Atlantis represents a milestone in the annals of archaeology and a testament to the enduring allure of ancient mysteries. May this document serve as a beacon of knowledge and inspiration for future generations of scholars and explorers.

Sincerely,
Dr. Theodore Westfield
Lead Archaeologist
Royal Society for Antiquities

Answer the following questions based on the document provided. You will be considering the vocabulary words practiced and evaluating the document in these terms.

1. How can you determine if this document is accurate and reliable?

_____

_____

_____

2. Does this document contain a chronological order of events and if so, what are they?

_____

_____

_____

3. What historical context does this document refer to?

_____

_____

_____

4. In what context does Professor Westfield encourage rigor?

_____

_____

_____

5. What tone does this document have? Is it formal or informal? How accessible is this document to people who are not familiar with the subject?

_____

_____

_____

22

Refer to page 230 for examples of valid answers.

Read the article below, written by a journalist who has made some spelling mistakes. Your task is to identify these errors and write down the correct spelling of each word. Look closely, as some mistakes may not be obvious at first glance.

The Great American Pizza Quest

In the grand context of life's many mysteries, like why socks disappear in the dryer, some things remain rigorosly rieliable, like pizza on a Friday night. Imagine a world where pizza wasn't as acessible as pressing a few buttons on your phone. Back in the day, you had to make a rigoros journey through the wilds of the untamed suburbs, battling traffic and the elements, all in search of that cheesy treasure. Today, thanks to the reiliable nature of modern technology, our quest for pizza requires less heroism but retains all the satisfaction. This shift in accesibility has made it so that the most strenuous effort we face is possibly choosing toppings—a challenge we bravely accept. In this humorous contects, it's clear that while our adventures may have changed, our love for easily obtained delights remains as fervent as ever.

Congratulations on finishing your first lesson!

Ready to groove to some electrifying party beats while practicing your spelling words from this lesson? It's all about enjoying the journey while honing your skills. Dive in and let's get started! **For optimal user experience, it is recommended to play the game on a computer or tablet and click the full-screen icon before starting the game.**

 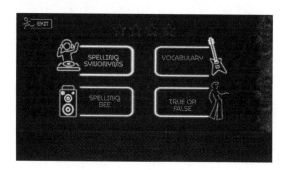

Copy this link on your browser:

https://natashascripts.com/musical-words/

or scan the code on your tablet

Password to enter: MelodyMaze1

Accurate, Reliable, Chronological, Context, Convey, Rigorous, Accessible

1. What new word did you find most interesting in lesson 1, and why?

----

2. Which part of lesson 1 was challenging for you? How did you overcome it, or what could you do differently next time?

----

3. Applying new vocabulary in real-life situations can greatly improve your understanding and retention of these words. Try using at least one of the new words you learned today in your daily life with the ideas below.

a. Create a sentence using "accessible" to describe your favorite website or app. Why do you find it easy to use?

b. Using "rigorous" in a sentence, describe a hobby or sport that requires a lot of effort and precision.

c. Write a sentence with "reliable" about a person or gadget that you always count on. What makes them or it so dependable?

d. Write a sentence featuring "context" related to a news story or historical event you recently learned about. How does understanding the background help explain what happened?

In our upcoming lessons, we'll dive into new word sets crucial for broadening your spelling and vocabulary skills, aimed at enhancing your ability to communicate more clearly and effectively. Our main goal will be to master these words—grasping their spellings and learning to use them effectively in context. Here are the words you can look forward to exploring in our next lesson: **Assess, Criteria, Vulnerabilities, Fortify, Decipher, Conceal, Ambiguous, Formulating, Desolate, Exhausted, Empathy, Alleviate.**

Take a moment to think about your learning objectives for these new words and then use the space below to outline your goals and plan how to achieve them. Ask yourself the following questions: **(i) What do I want to achieve with each of these new words?** (E.g., Understand their meanings, use them in sentences, improve spelling); **(ii) How will I learn these words?** (Consider making your own flashcards, making sentences, daily practice, using them in conversations, etc.); **(iii) How will I measure my success?** (Being able to spell all the words correctly, using each word in a sentence, etc.).

Word	My Goal	My Strategy	Deadline
Example: vulnerable	Spell and use in context	Flashcards, practice, daily journal, etc.	End of the week

Lesson 2

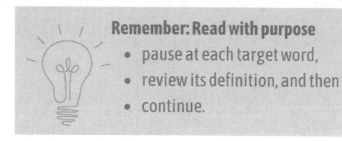

Remember: Read with purpose
- pause at each target word,
- review its definition, and then
- continue.

Cybersecurity

In the realm of cybersecurity, professionals regularly **assess** the strength and resilience of digital infrastructures against potential cyber-attacks. The assessment process relies on a comprehensive set of **criteria**, including the robustness of firewalls, the effectiveness of encryption methods, the rigor of access controls, and the employees' awareness of phishing tactics. These criteria are crucial in identifying **vulnerabilities** within the system and determining the necessary measures to **fortify** security.

Target Word Definitions

Assess: To evaluate or examine something carefully to understand its value or quality.

Criteria: Standards or rules used to judge or make decisions about something.

Vulnerabilities: Weaknesses or gaps that can be exploited or harmed, especially in a system or security.

Fortify: To strengthen or reinforce something, making it more secure or resistant to attack.

Identify two additional words from the passage that you wish to further practice, focusing on their meanings or spellings.

Spelling	Definition

Assess	as - sess	--
Criteria	cri - te - ri - a	--
Vulnerabilities	vul - ner - a -bil - i - ties	--
Fortify	for - ti - fy	--
		--

The Dead Sea Scrolls

The discovery of the Dead Sea Scrolls in the mid-20th century offered scholars a rare opportunity to **decipher** texts that had been **concealed** for nearly two millennia. These ancient manuscripts contained a mix of biblical and non-biblical writings, some of which presented **ambiguous** accounts of religious practices and beliefs of the time. Researchers were tasked with **formulating** hypotheses on the origins and significance of these texts, using various criteria to determine their authenticity and place within the historical context of Judaism and early Christianity. The scrolls, found in caves near the Dead Sea, have since shed invaluable light on the linguistic, religious, and cultural landscape of the ancient Near East, though debates about their full implications continue to this day.

Target Word Definitions

Decipher: To figure out the meaning of something that is hard to understand or read.

Concealed: Hidden from view or kept secret.

Ambiguous: Unclear or having more than one possible meaning or interpretation.

Formulating (formulate): Creating or developing a plan or strategy in a detailed and careful way.

List three other words from the passage that you want to practice for meaning or spelling.

Spelling   Meaning and Definition

------------------------   ---

------------------------   ---

------------------------   ---

$\longrightarrow$

Decipher   -------------------------   -------------------------------

Concealed   -------------------------   -------------------------------

Ambiguous   -------------------------   -------------------------------

Formulating   -------------------------   -------------------------------

The Aquila Earthquake

In the wake of the devastating earthquake that struck L'Aquila, Italy, in 2009, the city was left in a **desolate** state. The crumbled buildings mirrored the despair that its inhabitants had experienced. Rescue teams, though physically **exhausted** from their relentless search through the rubble, were driven by a deep sense of **empathy** for the victims and their families. Efforts to **alleviate** the immediate suffering included setting up temporary shelters, providing medical care, and distributing essential supplies.

Target Word Definitions

Desolate: Very empty and sad, often because of being abandoned or destroyed.

Exhausted: Extremely tired or drained of energy.

Empathy: The ability to understand and share the feelings of another person.

Alleviate: To make something, like pain or suffering, less severe or more bearable.

🖉   ⟶

Desolate   des - o - late   _____

Exhausted   ex - haust - ed   _____

Empathy   em - pa - thy   _____

Alleviate   al - le - vi - ate   _____

🖉   ⟶

Assess   _____   _____

Criteria   _____   _____

Vulnerabilities   _____   _____

Fortify   _____   _____

Decipher   _____   _____

Concealed   _____   _____

Ambiguous   _____   _____

Formulating   _____   _____

Desolate   _____   _____

Exhausted   _____   _____

Empathy   _____   _____

Alleviate   _____   _____

✏️ **Define in Context: Carefully read each sentence and respond to the subsequent question.**

1. Before making a decision, the teacher needed to assess each student's project based on originality and effort.

What does it mean to "assess" a project?

----

2. The competition's criteria included creativity, technique, and presentation.

What are "criteria" in the context of a competition?

3.Without its protective case, the smartphone was vulnerable to scratches and damage.

Why is something described as "vulnerable"?

----

4. The city decided to fortify its flood defenses in response to the increasing water levels.

What does it mean to "fortify" something?

----

5. Archaeologists had to decipher the ancient text to understand its historical significance.

What does "decipher" involve when dealing with ancient texts?

----

6. The spy had to conceal the documents carefully to avoid detection.

What does it mean to "conceal" something?

----

7. The directions were ambiguous, leaving the hikers unsure of which path to take.

Why might "ambiguous" directions be problematic?

----

8. The scientist took weeks to formulate a hypothesis that could be tested experimentally.

What does "formulate" involve in the context of scientific research?

----

9. After the storm, the beach looked desolate, with debris everywhere and no people in sight.

What kind of scene does "desolate" describe?

----

10. After the marathon, the runners were completely exhausted, barely able to walk.

How does someone feel when they are "exhausted"?

----

11. Showing empathy, the counselor listened carefully to the student's concerns, understanding her feelings.

Why is "empathy" important in a counseling session?

----

12. The medicine was prescribed to alleviate the symptoms of the flu, making the patient feel better.

What is the purpose of taking medicine to "alleviate" symptoms?

Refer to page 230-231 for examples of valid answers.

✏ **Can you decode the scrambled words and discover the hidden mystery word?**

T I I R R A E C

S A S E S S

U N R A V E L B L E

G U M B O A S U I

C H I R P E E D

R T Y O F F I

C L E C O N A

Clue: I dine in darkness and work unseen, in your walls and floors I reign as queen. What am I?

_____

Self-Reflection

Assess, Criteria, Vulnerabilities, Fortify, Decipher, Concealed, Ambiguous, Formulating, Desolate, Exhausted, Empathy, Alleviate.

1. What new words did you find most interesting in this lesson?

----

2. Did you encounter any words that were particularly challenging to spell?

----

3. How can you address and overcome these challenges in future lessons?

----

4. What strategies worked best for you in learning and remembering new words?

----

5. Did you achieve your spelling and vocabulary goals for this lesson? If not, how can you improve for the next one?

Here are the words you'll be learning in the next lesson:

Coalesce   **Elucidate**

Disparage   **Convey**

Commensurate   **Empirical**

Anecdote   **Arbitrate**

Formulate   **Authenticate**

Differentiate

Remember:
- Define Objectives: understand meanings, use in sentences, improve spelling.
- Plan Your Learning Approach: flashcards, write sentences, practice daily, use words in conversations.
- Measure Your Success:
  - Spell all words correctly.
  - Successfully use each word in a sentence.

Word	My Goal	My Strategy	Deadline
Example: disparage	Spell and use in context	Flashcards, practice, daily journal, etc.	End of the week

Lesson 3

Begin by reading the sentence provided, which includes the target word. Next, review the definition given below the sentence to understand the word's meaning. Then, in the space provided, break down the word into its syllables and complete the spelling drill.

---

1. Over the course of the afternoon, the various ideas from the brainstorming session began to **coalesce** into a clear, comprehensive plan for the project.

Definition of "Coalesce": To come together to form one group or mass.

co - a - lesce → _____ _____ _____

coalesce → _____ _____ _____

---

2. In her presentation, Lauren **elucidated** the complex theory by using clear examples.

Definition of "Elucidate": To explain or make something clear.

e - lu - ci - date → _____ _____ _____

elucidate (elucidated) → _____ _____ _____

3. Brittany was disheartened to overhear her classmates **disparaging** her History Day Project.

Definition of "Disparage": To speak in a way that shows you do not respect or value someone or something.

dis - par - age ⟶ _____   _____   _____

disparage (disparaging) ⟶ _____   _____   _____

4. In her English essay, Emma aimed to **convey** the importance of courage through the protagonist's journey in the novel they were studying

Definition of "Convey": To communicate or express something, with or without using words.

con - vey ⟶ _____   _____   _____

convey ⟶ _____   _____   _____

5. Logan felt that the amount of homework assigned was not **commensurate** with the time given to complete it, leaving him overwhelmed.

Definition of "Commensurate": Matching something in size, importance, quality, etc.

com - men - su - rate ⟶ _____   _____   _____

commensurate ⟶ _____   _____   _____

Remember: Read with purpose
- pause at each target word,
- review its definition, and then
- continue.

During Class

1. In their science class, the students embarked on an **empirical** study to observe plant growth under different light conditions. Working in small groups, they were tasked to **formulate** hypotheses about which light condition would be most conducive to growth. As the experiment progressed, they meticulously recorded their observations, learning to **differentiate** between the subtle changes in plant height and health.

2. During history class, Mrs. Miller shared an amusing **anecdote** about a famous historical figure to capture her students' attention. The story involved a dispute over land that required a neutral party to **arbitrate** and make a fair decision. To prove the truth of her story, Mrs. Miller showed the class an **authenticated** document from the time period, complete with the original signatures of those involved. This helped the students understand the importance of authenticated documents in historical research.

Target Word Definitions

Empirical: Based on experiments or experience rather than ideas or theories.

Formulate: To create or prepare something carefully, paying attention to details.

Differentiate: To recognize or show the difference between two or more things.

Anecdote: A short, amusing or interesting story about a real incident or person.

Arbitrate: To make a decision about a disagreement or settle a dispute.

Authenticate (authenticated): To prove that something is real, true, or what people say it is.

List any other words from the passages you want to practice for meaning or spelling.

Spelling   **Definition**

----------------------   ---

----------------------   ---

----------------------   ---

Breaking down words into syllables helps you understand the structure and rhythm of words, making spelling easier and more accurate.

Empirical   em - pir - i - cal   _____   _____

Formulate   for - mu - late   _____   _____

Differentiate   dif - fer - en - ti - ate _____   _____

Anecdote   an - ec - dote   _____   _____

Arbitrate   ar - bi - trate   _____   _____

Authenticate   au - then - ti - cate   _____   _____

Now write each word in full.

Empirical   _____   _____   _____

Formulate   _____   _____   _____

Differentiate   _____   _____   _____

Anecdote   _____   _____   _____

Arbitrate   _____   _____   _____

Authenticate   _____   _____   _____

My List of Words

--------------------------   --------------------------   --------------------------

--------------------------   --------------------------   --------------------------

--------------------------   --------------------------   --------------------------

--------------------------   --------------------------   --------------------------

Reflective Writing: Write a reflective response to the following prompts using your own experiences, examples and observations to support your answers. Here is an example:

Share a personal anecdote that taught you an important lesson or perspective.

Last summer, I forgot my lines during the school play. It was embarrassing, but I learned to laugh at myself and not take things too seriously. This experience taught me that making mistakes is part of learning and it's okay to not be perfect all the time.

1. Can you recall a time when different ideas or perspectives **coalesced** to create a successful outcome?

_____

_____

_____

2. Describe a situation where someone's ability to **elucidate** complex information helped you understand it better.

_____

_____

_____

3. Reflect on a time when you felt **disparaged** by someone's comments. How did you handle the situation?

_____

_____

_____

4. Can you share an example of a piece of artwork or music that effectively **conveys** a specific emotion or message?

_____

_____

_____

5. Consider a recent accomplishment or achievement. Do you feel the recognition or reward you received was **commensurate** with your efforts? Why or why not?

_____

_____

_____

6. Have you ever conducted an **empirical** experiment or observation? What did you learn from the experience?

_____

_____

_____

7. Share a personal **anecdote** that taught you an important lesson or perspective.

_____

_____

_____

8. Have you ever been in a situation where you had to **arbitrate** a disagreement between friends or family members? How did you approach it?

_____

_____

_____

9. Think about a recent problem or challenge you encountered. How did you **formulate** a plan to address it?

_____

_____

_____

10. Have you ever questioned the **authenticity** of information you came across online or in a book? How did you verify its accuracy?

_____

_____

_____

11. How do you **differentiate** between reliable and unreliable sources of information?

_____

_____

Well done on finishing the initial three lessons!

Now is an ideal time to take a brief break from this workbook and embark on an exciting spelling and vocabulary adventure with Gabi and Brad, the protagonists of our story. Gabi and Brad, two teenage siblings, require your assistance in navigating a dense, expansive forest to locate a secluded cottage. This hidden sanctuary represents their sole chance of evading the drug dealers threatening their family's safety.

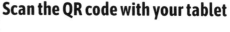

Scan the QR code with your tablet

Or

Copy and paste the link below on your browser

https://tinyurl.com/Escapetosafehaven

Before you begin:

1. Read the story, then click the link at the bottom of the page to start your first challenge, "The Dense Forest."

2. Complete the quiz and submit your answers. You'll receive a notification with a link to view your results and another link to continue to the next part of the story. Both links will open in new tabs.

3. Review your answers to see where you need improvement before moving on to the next challenge.

4. Repeat these steps for each subsequent challenge.

Coalesce, Elucidate, Disparage, Convey, Commensurate, Empirical, Anecdote, Arbitrate, Formulate, Authenticate, Differentiate.

1. This lesson contained words with tricky letters such as the "s" and "c" in "coalesce". How can you ensure to remember these tricky letter positions in similar words?

----

2. Which words in this lesson posed challenges for you in both spelling and meaning?

----

3. What strategies or techniques could you use next time to overcome challenges with tricky words in both spelling and meaning?

Consider practicing syllabification of the challenging words, creating flashcards to highlight tricky letters, and using a spelling and writing journal.

In the next lesson, you'll be learning the following words: **Roam, Formidable, Bipedal, Verdant, Fossils, Crucial, Anatomy,** and **Extinction**.

As you prepare to learn these new words, remember to reflect on your learning objectives. Ask yourself questions such as:

- What do I want to achieve with each of these new words? (e.g., Understand their meanings, use them in sentences, improve spelling)
- How will I learn these words?
- How will I measure my success? (e.g., Being able to spell all the words correctly, using each word in a sentence)

Don't forget to practice with words from previous lessons to further reinforce your learning.

Word	My Goal	My Strategy	Deadline
Example: crucial	*spell correctly*	*Practicing the word daily, for five minutes.*	*End of the week*

Lesson 4

Remember: Read with purpose
- pause at each target word,
- review its definition, and then
- continue.

Dinosaurs of the Prehistoric Era

Millions of years ago, during the prehistoric era, dinosaurs **roamed** the Earth. These majestic creatures exhibited a range of characteristics, from their size and habitat to their diet. They were **formidable** predators such as Tyrannosaurus rex and Velociraptor, as well as colossal herbivores like Triceratops and Brachiosaurus. Some dinosaurs were **bipedal** and moved on two legs, while others were quadrupedal and traveled on four. They inhabited varied landscapes, spanning from **verdant** forests to expansive deserts. **Fossils** offer **crucial** insights into their **anatomy**, behavior, and eventual **extinction**.

Target Word Definitions

Roam: To move about or travel without a specific destination.

Formidable: Inspiring fear or respect due to size, strength, or power.

Bipedal: Walking or moving on two legs

Verdant: Green with vegetation.

Fossils: Remains or traces of ancient organisms preserved in rock.

Crucial: Extremely important or essential for success.

Anatomy: The structure of an organism's body, including its organs and tissues.

Extinction: The complete disappearance or eradication of a species from the Earth.

 List any other words from the passage you want to practice for meaning or spelling.

Spelling

Definition

_____   _____

_____   _____

✏️ Break down the words into syllables.

→ →

Roam	roam	_____	_____
Formidable	for - mi - da - ble	_____	_____
Bipedal	bi - pe - dal	_____	_____
Verdant	ver - dant	_____	_____
Fossils	fos - sils	_____	_____
Crucial	cru - cial	_____	_____
Anatomy	a - nat - o - my	_____	_____
Extinction	ex - tinc - tion	_____	_____

✏️ Now write each word in full.

Roam	_____	_____	_____
Formidable	_____	_____	_____
Bipedal	_____	_____	_____
Verdant	_____	_____	_____
Fossils	_____	_____	_____
Crucial	_____	_____	_____
Anatomy	_____	_____	_____
Extinction	_____	_____	_____

✏️ My List of Words

_____   _____   _____

_____   _____   _____

_____   _____   _____

_____   _____   _____

Rewriting sentences: Identify the word or phrase in each of the sentences that matches the definition in the list of target words. Then, rewrite the sentence using the target word.

Target Word Definitions

Roam: To move about or travel without a specific destination.

Formidable: Inspiring fear or respect due to size, strength, or power.

Bipedal: Walking or moving on two legs

Verdant: Green with vegetation.

Fossils: Remains or traces of ancient organisms preserved in rock.

Crucial: Extremely important or essential for success.

Anatomy: The structure of an organism's body, including its organs and tissues.

Extinction: The complete disappearance or eradication of a species from the Earth.

1. Two-legged animals, such as birds and humans, have evolved specialized skeletal structures and muscular systems to support their locomotion.

----

2. The lush meadow stretched out before us, vibrant with color and life.

----

3. The adventurer wandered through the dense jungle, exploring its mysteries.

----

4. Paleontologists study the preserved remains of ancient organisms to learn about prehistoric life.

----

5. The towering mountain loomed over the landscape, impressing all who beheld its majesty.

----

6. The Dodo, a flightless bird native to the island of Mauritius, has disappeared due to human activities and habitat destruction.

----

7. Scientists examine the physical structure and internal workings of living organisms to understand their biology.

----

8. Effective communication is essential for building strong relationships and fostering teamwork.

Roam: To move about or travel without a specific destination.

Formidable: Inspiring fear or respect due to size, strength, or power.

Bipedal: Walking or moving on two legs

Verdant: Green with vegetation.

Fossils: Remains or traces of ancient organisms preserved in rock.

Crucial: Extremely important or essential for success.

Anatomy: The structure of an organism's body, including its organs and tissues.

Extinction: The complete disappearance or eradication of a species from the Earth.

Choose three words from the list and write a sentence for each.

--------------------   --

--------------------   --

--------------------   --

Word Search Puzzle with a Twist. Find the target words practiced in this lesson. Then find the four hidden synonyms of the starred words and write them down in the spaces below. The words list below is in alphabetical order.

```
M E B S W G K F Y M O T A N A
D X I R V C D S N I A M E R Q
B T P D H R X I O Y E B L V B
Y I E G C I K J K X L Q J T F
F N D T N T F G U T V G J I O
D C A Z C I A D D E H B G E R
F T L R U C T O F L K K S U M
Y I Q R L A A A S A Z S D D I
T O P Q D L L L D O L Q K T D
N N L C X I I A D I L Y W A A
A A D R D S I V I A M H Y B B
D X F V S C M M G C L I S J L
R C P O S A D P A Y U R T U E
E R F W O S N Y Z T T R J N L
V C X R D C D L D W I H C Y I
```

ANATOMY   BIPEDAL   _____

★ CRUCIAL   EXTINCTION   ★ FORMIDABLE

★ FOSSILS   _____

_____   ROAM   ★ VERDANT

Roam, Formidable, Bipedal, Verdant, Fossils, Crucial, Anatomy, Extinction.

1. Which two words from this lesson do you anticipate using more frequently than the others?

----

2. Which part of the lesson do you feel was most beneficial to you, and why?

----

3. What is one action you can take after each lesson to review the words you find most challenging to spell and use in your writing? Explore the suggestions below to find an approach that suits you.

1. **Create Flashcards**: Write the challenging words on one side of a card and their definitions or sentences using the word in context on the other side. Review these flashcards regularly.
2. **Maintain a Vocabulary Journal**: Dedicate a journal or section of a notebook to new and challenging words. Include the word, its definition, and a sentence using it.
3. **Use the Words in Sentences**: Write original sentences using each challenging word. This not only helps with spelling but also with understanding how to use the words in context.
4. **Engage in Peer Quizzing**: Pair up with a classmate and quiz each other on the challenging words. You can take turns asking for the spelling of a word, its definition, or its use in a sentence.

The upcoming lesson will present a greater challenge as you'll be practicing 17 new words. By the end of this lesson, you'll have practiced a total of 57 words! Remember, while spelling and vocabulary practice isn't about numbers, it's definitely a satisfying achievement.

Here are the words for the next lesson to help you set your goals: **Hieroglyphics, Cuneiform, Stylus, Archaeologists, Artifacts, Devastate, Exacerbate, Pivotal, Severely, Decline, Spurred, Perpetrate, Coordinated, Collapse, Extremism, Resilience,** and **Adversity.**

Word	My Goal	My Strategy	Deadline
Example: archaeologists	Remember tricky "aeo"	Practicing the word in sentences.	End of the week
Example: perpetrate	Not to confuse it with "penetrate" and to practice its meaning	Use in sentences	End of the week

Lesson 5

Remember: Read with purpose
- pause at each target word,
- review its definition, and then
- continue.

Deciphering Ancient Writings

Ancient civilizations communicated and recorded their history through various means, notably through the use of **hieroglyphics** and **cuneiform** writing. Hieroglyphics, developed by the Egyptians, consisted of a complex system of pictorial symbols that represented objects, concepts, sounds, and later, more abstract ideas. Cuneiform, on the other hand, was invented by the Sumerians of ancient Mesopotamia. It was characterized by wedge-shaped marks made on clay tablets with a reed **stylus**. Both forms of writing are among the earliest known in human history and have provided scholars with valuable insights into the lives, beliefs, and practices of ancient peoples. **Archaeologists** have discovered numerous **artifacts** adorned with these writings, including stone monuments, pottery, and scrolls made of papyrus or leather. These artifacts are crucial for understanding our past, as they offer a tangible link to the thoughts and voices of civilizations that flourished thousands of years ago.

Target Word Definitions

Hyieroglyphics:	A system of writing using pictures and symbols, used in ancient Egypt to record information and stories.
Cuneiform:	One of the earliest forms of writing, invented by the Sumerians, characterized by wedge-shaped marks pressed into clay tablets with a stylus.
Stylus:	A pointed tool used for writing or engraving on various materials, such as clay or wax tablets, in ancient times.
Archaeologists:	Scientists who study past human life and cultures by examining physical remains, such as buildings, tools, and pottery.
Artifacts:	Objects made or used by humans, often from a past era, studied by archaeologists to understand history and prehistory.

✏️ **List any other words from the passage you want to practice for meaning or spelling.**

Spelling   Definition

-------------------   --------------------------------------

-------------------   --------------------------------------

-------------------   --------------------------------------

-------------------   --------------------------------------

✏️ **Break down the words into syllables.**

→   →

Hieroglyphics   hi - er - o - gly - phics   -------------------   -------------------

Cuneiform   cu - ne - i - form   -------------------   -------------------

Stylus   sty - lus   -------------------   -------------------

Archaeologists ar - che - ol - o - gists   -------------------   -------------------

Artifacts   ar - ti - facts   -------------------   -------------------

✏️ **Now write each word in full.**

→   →

Hieroglyphics   -------------------   -------------------   -------------------

Cuneiform   -------------------   -------------------   -------------------

Stylus   -------------------   -------------------   -------------------

Archaeologists -------------------   -------------------   -------------------

Artifacts   -------------------   -------------------   -------------------

✏️ **My List of Words**

-------------------   -------------------   -------------------

-------------------   -------------------   -------------------

-------------------   -------------------   -------------------

-------------------   -------------------   -------------------

Remember: Read with purpose
- pause at each target word,
- review its definition, and then
- continue.

The Black Death in Medieval Europe

The Black Death, a **devastating** pandemic in the mid-14th century, caused widespread death and societal upheaval across Europe, Asia, and Africa. This disease, transmitted by fleas on rats, spread rapidly via trade routes and within densely populated cities, **exacerbating** mortality rates and economic turmoil.

This pandemic marked a **pivotal** moment in medieval history, decimating communities, leading to significant labor shortages, and the decline of feudal systems. Economic activities were **severely** disrupted, exacerbating social unrest and economic **decline**. The Catholic Church's inability to halt the plague eroded its authority, sparking religious upheaval.

However, the aftermath of the Black Death also **spurred** positive changes. The labor shortages increased wages and mobility for serfs, contributing to the feudal system's decline and the emergence of a middle class and early capitalism. It also prompted advancements in medicine and public health in efforts to combat such diseases.

Target Word Definitions

Devastate: To cause great damage or destruction.

Exacerbate: To make a situation worse.

Pivotal: Crucially important or central.

Severely: Very seriously or harshly.

Decline: To decrease in quality, quantity, or strength.

Spur (spurred): To stimulate or encourage to action.

✎ **List any other words from the passage you want to practice for meaning or spelling.**

Spelling   Definition

-------------------   --

-------------------   --

-------------------   --

Break down the words into syllables.

→ →

Devastate	**dev - as - tate**	_____	_____
Exacerbate	**ex - ac - er - bate**	_____	_____
Pivotal	**piv - ot - al**	_____	_____
Severely	**se - vere - ly**	_____	_____
Decline	**de - cline**	_____	_____
Spurred	**spurred***	_____	_____

*one syllable

Now write each word in full.

Devastate	_____	_____	_____
Exacerbate	_____	_____	_____
Pivotal	_____	_____	_____
Severely	_____	_____	_____
Decline	_____	_____	_____
Spurred	_____	_____	_____

My List of Words

_____   _____   _____

_____   _____   _____

_____   _____   _____

_____   _____   _____

Remember: Read with purpose
- pause at each target word,
- review its definition, and then
- continue.

9/11: A Day of Tragedy and Tested Resilience

On September 11, 2001, al-Qaeda **perpetrated coordinated** terrorist attacks in the United States, targeting the World Trade Center in New York City and the Pentagon in Arlington, Virginia, using hijacked airplanes. This led to the devastating **collapse** of the Twin Towers and significant damage to the Pentagon, while Flight 93, overtaken by passengers resisting the terrorists, crashed in Pennsylvania.

These attacks caused nearly 3,000 deaths, marking it as the deadliest terrorist act in modern history. The impact spurred the U.S. to initiate a War on Terror and tighten global security measures. In the wake of 9/11, the world saw a shift in geopolitics and increased scrutiny on **extremism**. The **resilience** of nations was tested as they united in solidarity against terrorism, emphasizing prevention and strength in **adversity**.

Target Word Definitions

Perpetrate (perpetrated): To commit or carry out, typically a harmful, illegal, or immoral action.

*Coordinated: Organized or aligned effectively.

Collapse: To fall down or inward suddenly, often after failing to support weight or pressure.

Extremism: Holding extreme political or religious views that deviate from the norm or mainstream.

Resilience: The capacity to recover quickly from difficulties or adversity.

Adversity: Hardship, misfortune or challenging conditions.

*functions as an adjective in the passage, describing the terrorist attacks.

✎ **List any other words from the passage you want to practice for meaning or spelling.**

Spelling   Definition

------------------------   --

------------------------   --

------------------------   --

Break down the words into syllables.

→ →

Perpetrate	per - pe - trate	_____	_____
Coordinated	co - or - di - nat - ed	_____	_____
Collapse	col - lapse	_____	_____
Extremism	ex - trem - ism	_____	_____
Resilience	re - sil - ience	_____	_____
Adversity	ad - ver - si - ty	_____	_____

Now write each word in full.

Perpetrate	_____	_____	_____
Coordinated	_____	_____	_____
Collapse	_____	_____	_____
Extremism	_____	_____	_____
Resilience	_____	_____	_____
Adversity	_____	_____	_____

My List of Words

_____ _____ _____

_____ _____ _____

_____ _____ _____

_____ _____ _____

Finish this picture game by first going over the words and their meanings from this lesson. Match each image with the word that fits best and write the word correctly below it.

Select two images from the previous activity and write about them using one of the following writing styles:

1. Narrative: Telling stories or recounting events.

2. Expository: Explaining or informing about a topic.

3. Persuasive: Convincing the reader to adopt a viewpoint or take action.

4. Descriptive: Creating vivid images and sensory details.

5. Analytical: Examining a topic in depth and evaluating its significance.

6. Reflective: Personal introspection and reflection.

7. Creative: Imaginative expression through poetry, stories, plays and dialogues.

Example:

In the process of metamorphosis, a butterfly reaches a pivotal moment as it breaks free from its cocoon. This transformation involves significant internal restructuring, as the caterpillar sheds its old identity and embraces a new one.
(Expository Writing)

Image 1

Image 2

Lesson 6

Congratulations on finishing lesson 5!

Prepare for an exciting adventure with the Time Machine game. This adventure is designed to help you review the spelling and vocabulary words you've learned in Lessons 4 and 5 in a fun way.

As you step into the Time Machine, prepare to travel from the prehistoric age all the way to the present day. But there's a twist - to return to the present, you'll need to gather missing parts for the Time Machine scattered across different eras.

Your success on this journey hinges on your knowledge of spelling and word usage. At each stop through time, you'll face challenges requiring you to choose the correct spelling of words and how they are used in sentences. Each correct answer brings you one step closer to gathering all the necessary parts to repair the Time Machine and journey back to the present. **For optimal user experience, it is recommended to play the game on a computer or tablet and click the full-screen icon before starting the game.**

Enjoy the ride!

Scan the code on your tablet

or copy this link on your browser:
https://natashascripts.com/time-machine/

Password to enter: TemporalKey4-5

As we progress through our learning journey, it's essential to pause and reflect on the vocabulary we've encountered. This exercise is designed to help you assess your confidence in spelling and using the words you've learned from Lessons 1-6. By reviewing these words, you can identify which ones you've mastered and which ones might need more attention.

1. **Review the List:** Start by reading through the word list carefully. This will refresh your memory and help you start thinking about how each word is used.
2. **Rate Your Confidence:** For each word, rate your confidence on a scale of 1-5, in your ability to spell and use it correctly.
3. **Identify Focus Areas:**
   a. **Group the Words:** Organize the words into categories based on your confidence ratings. This will help you see patterns and decide which areas need the most work.
   b. **Set Priorities:** Focus on the words where your confidence is low. These are the ones that will benefit most from extra practice.
4. **Practice Actively**:
   a. **Use in Sentences:** Try to write sentences using the words you're less confident about. This helps in understanding context and usage.
   b. **Spelling Drills:** Conduct spelling drills on words you rated lower in confidence to improve your familiarity and accuracy.
   c. **Peer Review:** Pair up with a classmate to quiz each other on the words, discuss their meanings, and correct each other's sentences.
5. **Reflect**:
   a. **Self-Assessment**: After practicing, reassess your confidence levels. Note any improvements or ongoing challenges.
   b. **Plan Further Review**: For words that still challenge you, plan ongoing reviews, such as using them in daily journal entries or discussing them with friends and family.

Benefit from the Exercise: Engaging with this review will reinforce your learning and help ensure that these words become a solid part of your vocabulary, enhancing both your writing and speaking skills. Remember, the goal isn't just to pass a test but to genuinely own the words you learn and use them effortlessly in your daily life.

Each list page is followed by a dedicated notes page for you to use and jot down your lists, sentences, and reflections.

List of Words Practiced	How confident do I feel about spelling each word correctly?	How confident do I feel about using each word in a sentence correctly?	Which words do I need to practice more?
mediator	○ ○ ○ ○ ○	○ ○ ○ ○ ○	
bipedal	○ ○ ○ ○ ○	○ ○ ○ ○ ○	
fossils	○ ○ ○ ○ ○	○ ○ ○ ○ ○	
hieroglyphics	○ ○ ○ ○ ○	○ ○ ○ ○ ○	
cuneiform	○ ○ ○ ○ ○	○ ○ ○ ○ ○	
artifacts	○ ○ ○ ○ ○	○ ○ ○ ○ ○	
devastating	○ ○ ○ ○ ○	○ ○ ○ ○ ○	
pivotal	○ ○ ○ ○ ○	○ ○ ○ ○ ○	
decline	○ ○ ○ ○ ○	○ ○ ○ ○ ○	
perpetrate	○ ○ ○ ○ ○	○ ○ ○ ○ ○	
exacerbate	○ ○ ○ ○ ○	○ ○ ○ ○ ○	
resilience	○ ○ ○ ○ ○	○ ○ ○ ○ ○	

List of Words Practiced	How confident do I feel about spelling each word correctly?	How confident do I feel about using each word in a sentence correctly?	Which words do I need to practice more?
accurate	○ ○ ○ ○ ○	○ ○ ○ ○ ○	
reliable	○ ○ ○ ○ ○	○ ○ ○ ○ ○	
chronological	○ ○ ○ ○ ○	○ ○ ○ ○ ○	
context	○ ○ ○ ○ ○	○ ○ ○ ○ ○	
convey	○ ○ ○ ○ ○	○ ○ ○ ○ ○	
rigorous	○ ○ ○ ○ ○	○ ○ ○ ○ ○	
accessible	○ ○ ○ ○ ○	○ ○ ○ ○ ○	
assess	○ ○ ○ ○ ○	○ ○ ○ ○ ○	
criteria	○ ○ ○ ○ ○	○ ○ ○ ○ ○	
vulnerabilities	○ ○ ○ ○ ○	○ ○ ○ ○ ○	
fortify	○ ○ ○ ○ ○	○ ○ ○ ○ ○	
decipher	○ ○ ○ ○ ○	○ ○ ○ ○ ○	
conceal	○ ○ ○ ○ ○	○ ○ ○ ○ ○	
ambiguous	○ ○ ○ ○ ○	○ ○ ○ ○ ○	
formulating	○ ○ ○ ○ ○	○ ○ ○ ○ ○	
desolate	○ ○ ○ ○ ○	○ ○ ○ ○ ○	
exhausted	○ ○ ○ ○ ○	○ ○ ○ ○ ○	
empathy	○ ○ ○ ○ ○	○ ○ ○ ○ ○	

73

List of Words Practiced	How confident do I feel about spelling each word correctly?	How confident do I feel about using each word in a sentence correctly?	Which words do I need to practice more?
coalesce	○ ○ ○ ○ ○	○ ○ ○ ○ ○	
elucidate	○ ○ ○ ○ ○	○ ○ ○ ○ ○	
disparage	○ ○ ○ ○ ○	○ ○ ○ ○ ○	
stylus	○ ○ ○ ○ ○	○ ○ ○ ○ ○	
convey	○ ○ ○ ○ ○	○ ○ ○ ○ ○	
commensurate	○ ○ ○ ○ ○	○ ○ ○ ○ ○	
empirical	○ ○ ○ ○ ○	○ ○ ○ ○ ○	
anecdote	○ ○ ○ ○ ○	○ ○ ○ ○ ○	
arbitrate	○ ○ ○ ○ ○	○ ○ ○ ○ ○	
formulate	○ ○ ○ ○ ○	○ ○ ○ ○ ○	
authenticate	○ ○ ○ ○ ○	○ ○ ○ ○ ○	
differentiate	○ ○ ○ ○ ○	○ ○ ○ ○ ○	
roam	○ ○ ○ ○ ○	○ ○ ○ ○ ○	
formidable	○ ○ ○ ○ ○	○ ○ ○ ○ ○	
bipedal	○ ○ ○ ○ ○	○ ○ ○ ○ ○	
verdant	○ ○ ○ ○ ○	○ ○ ○ ○ ○	
fossils	○ ○ ○ ○ ○	○ ○ ○ ○ ○	
crucial	○ ○ ○ ○ ○	○ ○ ○ ○ ○	

List of Words Practiced	How confident do I feel about spelling each word correctly?	How confident do I feel about using each word in a sentence correctly?	Which words do I need to practice more?
anatomy	○ ○ ○ ○ ○	○ ○ ○ ○ ○	
extinction	○ ○ ○ ○ ○	○ ○ ○ ○ ○	
archaeologists	○ ○ ○ ○ ○	○ ○ ○ ○ ○	
severely	○ ○ ○ ○ ○	○ ○ ○ ○ ○	
coordinated	○ ○ ○ ○ ○	○ ○ ○ ○ ○	
collapse	○ ○ ○ ○ ○	○ ○ ○ ○ ○	
extremism	○ ○ ○ ○ ○	○ ○ ○ ○ ○	
adversity	○ ○ ○ ○ ○	○ ○ ○ ○ ○	
spurred	○ ○ ○ ○ ○	○ ○ ○ ○ ○	
My List of Words			
	○ ○ ○ ○ ○	○ ○ ○ ○ ○	
	○ ○ ○ ○ ○	○ ○ ○ ○ ○	
	○ ○ ○ ○ ○	○ ○ ○ ○ ○	
	○ ○ ○ ○ ○	○ ○ ○ ○ ○	
	○ ○ ○ ○ ○	○ ○ ○ ○ ○	
	○ ○ ○ ○ ○	○ ○ ○ ○ ○	
	○ ○ ○ ○ ○	○ ○ ○ ○ ○	
	○ ○ ○ ○ ○	○ ○ ○ ○ ○	

My List of Words	How confident do I feel about spelling each word correctly?	How confident do I feel about using each word in a sentence correctly?	Which words do I need to practice more?
	○ ○ ○ ○ ○	○ ○ ○ ○ ○	
	○ ○ ○ ○ ○	○ ○ ○ ○ ○	
	○ ○ ○ ○ ○	○ ○ ○ ○ ○	
	○ ○ ○ ○ ○	○ ○ ○ ○ ○	
	○ ○ ○ ○ ○	○ ○ ○ ○ ○	
	○ ○ ○ ○ ○	○ ○ ○ ○ ○	
	○ ○ ○ ○ ○	○ ○ ○ ○ ○	
	○ ○ ○ ○ ○	○ ○ ○ ○ ○	
	○ ○ ○ ○ ○	○ ○ ○ ○ ○	
	○ ○ ○ ○ ○	○ ○ ○ ○ ○	
	○ ○ ○ ○ ○	○ ○ ○ ○ ○	
	○ ○ ○ ○ ○	○ ○ ○ ○ ○	
	○ ○ ○ ○ ○	○ ○ ○ ○ ○	
	○ ○ ○ ○ ○	○ ○ ○ ○ ○	
	○ ○ ○ ○ ○	○ ○ ○ ○ ○	
	○ ○ ○ ○ ○	○ ○ ○ ○ ○	
	○ ○ ○ ○ ○	○ ○ ○ ○ ○	
	○ ○ ○ ○ ○	○ ○ ○ ○ ○	

Here are the words you'll be learning in the next lesson:

Exposition, Excerpt, Depict, Incoherent, Mediate, Correlate, Bias, Feign, Exploit, Compromise.

Remember:
- Define Objectives: understand meanings, use in sentences, improve spelling.
- Plan Your Learning Approach: flashcards, write sentences, practice daily, use words in conversations.
- Measure Your Success:
  - Spell all words correctly.
  - Successfully use each word in a sentence.

Word	My Goal	My Strategy	Deadline

Lesson 7

Begin by reading the sentence provided, which includes the target word. Next, review the definition given below the sentence to understand the word's meaning. Then, in the space provided, break down the word into its syllables and complete the spelling drill.

1. The movie's **exposition**, which details the challenges and fears encountered by the crew of Apollo 13 during their mission to the moon, rivaled the excitement of Neil Armstrong's historic first attempt to land on the lunar surface.

Definition of "Exposition" : A technique that introduces background information about a story's setting, characters, and events, providing essential context to the audience.

ex - po - si - tion ⟶ _____ _____ _____

exposition ⟶ _____ _____ _____

2. During the history lecture, the professor read an **excerpt** from "Freedom's Dominion" by Jefferson Cowie, sparking a lively discussion about the clash between white people and American federal authority **depicted** in the book.

Definition of "Excerpt": A passage or selection taken from a larger work, such as a book, article, or speech, for the purpose of quoting, summarizing, or illustrating specific points.

ex - cerpt ⟶ _____ _____ _____

excerpt ⟶ _____ _____ _____

Definition of "Depict": To represent or describe something in words or images.

de - pict ⟶ _____ _____ _____

depict ⟶ _____ _____ _____

3. During episodes of low blood sugar, a person with diabetes may experience **incoherent** speech and confusion.

Definition of "Incoherent": Lacking clarity or logical connection.

in - co - her - ent ⟶ _____ _____ _____

incoherent ⟶ _____ _____ _____

4. The experienced diplomat was called upon to **mediate** the delicate negotiations between the two countries, aiming to facilitate a lasting peace agreement.

Definition of "Mediate": To help resolve a dispute between parties.

me - di - ate ⟶ _____ _____ _____

mediate ⟶ _____ _____ _____

5. The research study uncovered a fascinating **correlation** between students' sleep patterns and their academic performance, shedding light on the importance of rest for cognitive function.

Definition of "Correlation": The relationship or connection between two or more variables, often measured by how they change together.

cor - re - late ⟶ _____ _____ _____

correlate ⟶ _____ _____ _____

6. The news channel's **bias** toward a particular political party renders it unreliable as a source of impartial information.

Definition of "Bias": A tendency to favor a person, group or thing compared with another, often considered to be unfair.

bi - as →	_____ _____ _____
bias →	_____ _____ _____

7. During the surprise party, Jenn had to **feign** surprise because she had accidentally discovered the plan days earlier.

Definition of "Feign": To pretend to be affected by (a feeling, state or injury).

*feign →	_____ _____ _____
feign →	_____ _____ _____

* one syllable

8. The company was criticized for trying to **exploit** the natural resources of the forest without considering the environmental impact.

Definition of "Exploit": To make use of a resource or information for one's advantage, often in an unfair or unethical way.

ex - ploit →	_____ _____ _____
exploit →	_____ _____ _____

9. To reach an agreement, both parties had to **compromise**, each giving up something to settle their differences.

Definition of "Compromise": An agreement or settlement of a dispute that is reached by each side adjusting their demands or positions.
com - pro - mise ⟶ _____ _____ _____
compromise ⟶ _____ _____ _____

Observing tricky letters helps you identify specific areas where you struggle with spelling, enabling you to focus your efforts on those particular letters. This awareness allows you to develop strategies for better retention and accuracy in spelling.

Observation: Look closely at each target word below. Circle any letters you find tricky to remember.

Exposition

Excerpt

Depict

Incoherent

Correlate

Mediate

Bias

Feign

Exploit

Compromise

Proofreading: Read the paragraphs below containing spelling errors. Your task is to identify these errors and write down the correct spelling of each word in the spaces below. Look closely, as some mistakes may not be obvious at first glance.

1. The local art gallery's latest exposision was a breathtaking journey through the Renaissance period, showcasing paintings that vividly depikt the era's social dinamics and cultural richness. Among the displayed works, an ecxerpt from a lesser-known artist's dairy provided a facinating insight into the creative process behind these masterpieces. Visitors were captivated, feeling as though they had stepped back in time to witnes the birth of some of history's most revered art. (*7 spelling errors*)

2. When Tim attempted to medaite the dispute between his two cats over the sunny spot on the windowsill, he realized diplomacy was a tough sell in the feline world. Drawing on his best negociation tactics, he proposed a compromize: a schedule that allowed each cat exclusive sunbating rights for half the day. However, his plans were met with incoherant meows that seemed to question his sanity. In a surprising turn of events, the cats decided to exploite the situation by ignoring Tim entirely and squishing together in the sunny spot, proving that sometimes, the best solution is just finding a way to fit on the windowsill, no matter how tight the squeeze. (6 *spelling errors*)

3. During the debate competision, one team presented a compeling argument that challenged the prevailing bais in environmental policies. Using exerpts from scientific studies and historical data, they illustrated the corelation between industrial explotation and climate change. Their presentation, though initially met with skepticism, gradually won the audience over, demonstrating the power of well-researched arguments to medaite change in public opinion. (7 *spelling errors*)

Congratulations on finishing Lesson 7!

Are you ready to test your skills and assist a sorrowful spirit confined to an old mansion? Welcome to the interactive escape room "The Trapped Ghost"! This ghost, once a loving father, has been tormented by the loss of his cherished daughter. Her untimely departure has bound his soul to the house, leaving him in a perpetual search for peace.

As you step into the dimly lit corridors and explore the ancient chambers of the mansion, your journey will be met with a series of spelling and vocabulary challenges. Each puzzle you solve brings you closer to uncovering hidden items within the mansion's walls, each an essential piece in the puzzle of the ghost's fragmented memories. Your goal is to discover four artifacts that will gradually help recover the ghost's lost memories.

Are you ready to unlock the mysteries of "The Trapped Ghost" and release a soul from its earthly bonds? The doors to the mansion are open, and the quest for liberation begins now.

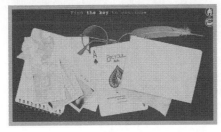 

Scan the code on your tablet

or copy this link on your browser:
https://natashascripts.com/the-trapped-ghost/

Password to enter: MemoryUnlock7

1. Reflect on your understanding of the words practiced in lesson 7. Can you define each word accurately?

Incoherent: _____

Mediate: _____

Correlate: _____

Bias: _____

Feign: _____

Exploit: _____

Compromise: _____

2. Think about your ability to recognize bias in different forms of media or communication. Can you identify instances of bias in news articles, advertisements, or social media posts?

_____

_____

_____

3. Reflect on your understanding of the word "mediate." Can you describe a situation where mediation might be necessary, and explain the role of a mediator?

_____

_____

_____

4. Consider the concept of compromise. Can you think of a recent situation where compromise was needed to resolve a conflict or disagreement?

_____

_____

_____

Here are the words you'll be learning in the next lesson:

Prevalent, Affiliation, Eminent, Audacious, Censure, Constrain, Intercede, Falter, Cynic.

Remember:
- Define Objectives: understand meanings, use in sentences, improve spelling.
- Plan Your Learning Approach: flashcards, write sentences, practice daily, use words in conversations.
- Measure Your Success:
  - Spell all words correctly.
  - Successfully use each word in a sentence.

Word	My Goal	My Strategy	Deadline

Lesson 8

Section 1: Application and Writing Integration

Start by reading the definitions of the target words. Then, fill each sentence with the appropriate word. Use each word in two different sentences.

Prevalent: Common, widespread, or occurring frequently.
Affiliation: A connection or association with a group, organization, or cause.
Eminent: Distinguished or noteworthy, standing out in a particular field or area.
Audacious: Bold, daring, fearless, often willing to take risks or venture into new territory.

1. Benjamin Franklin was an _____ figure in American history, known for his contributions as a founding father, inventor, and diplomat.

2. Cyberbullying has become _____ on social media platforms, posing significant challenges for educators and parents.

3. His _____ plan to revolutionize the industry raised eyebrows but ultimately proved successful.

4. Professor Stephen Hawking was an _____ physicist whose groundbreaking work on black holes and cosmology revolutionized our understanding of the universe.

5. In college settings, sports _____ can deeply influence students' identities and social experiences on campus.

6. In recent years, obesity has become _____, with over 40% of adults and nearly 20% of children affected by this health condition.

7. During the Revolutionary War, George Washington's _____ crossing of the Delaware River in 1776 surprised and defeated Hessian troops, boosting morale and reinvigorating the Continental Army.

8. _____ with professional organizations can enhance networking opportunities and career advancement prospects for individuals in various industries.

Censure: To express strong disapproval or criticism.
Constrain: To restrict or limit someone or something.
Intercede: To intervene or mediate on behalf of someone in a dispute or conflict.
Falter: To hesitate or stumble in speech or action, often due to uncertainty; to lose strength or momentum.
Cynic: Someone who distrusts the motives of others and believes that people are generally selfish or dishonest.

1. Despite early setbacks, Abraham Lincoln refused to _____ in his commitment to preserving the Union during the American Civil War.

2. The United Nations often seeks to _____ in conflicts around the world to promote peace and prevent further violence.

3. In 1954, the United States Senate voted to _____ Senator Joseph McCarthy for his controversial tactics during the anti-communist investigations known as the McCarthy era.

4. The Roman Empire began to _____ in the 3rd century AD due to economic decline, internal strife, and external invasions.

5. As a _____, Joe doubted the sincerity of politicians' promises, believing they were motivated solely by self-interest.

6. The Treaty of Versailles, signed in 1919, _____ Germany with harsh reparations and territorial losses, fueling resentment and laying the groundwork for World War II.

7. Social workers frequently _____ on behalf of vulnerable populations, advocating for their rights and access to resources in modern societies.

8. The Roman Senate issued a formal _____ against Julius Caesar for his actions as consul, leading to his eventual crossing of the Rubicon and the start of the Roman Civil War.

9. Growing up in a poverty-stricken neighborhood, Susan became a _____, distrusting institutions that failed to address the systemic issues plaguing her community.

10. The Great Depression _____ economic growth worldwide, leading to widespread unemployment, poverty, and social upheaval throughout the 1930s.

Remember:
- **Spot Tricky Letters**
- **Focus Your Efforts**
- **Develop Strategies**

Observation: Look closely at each target word below. Circle any letters you find tricky to remember.

Prevalent   Affiliation   Eminent

Audacious   Censure   Constrain

Intercede   Falter   Cynic

✏ **Break down the words into syllables .**

→   →

Prevalent	prev - a - lent	_____	_____
Affiliation	af - fil - i - a - tion	_____	_____
Eminent	em - i - nent	_____	_____
Audacious	au - da - cious	_____	_____
Censure	cen - sure	_____	_____
Constrain	con - strain	_____	_____
Intercede	in - ter - cede	_____	_____
Falter	fal - ter	_____	_____
Cynic	cyn - ic	_____	_____

✏ **Now write each word in full.**

Prevalent	_____	_____	_____
Affiliation	_____	_____	_____
Eminent	_____	_____	_____
Audacious	_____	_____	_____
Censure	_____	_____	_____
Constrain	_____	_____	_____
Intercede	_____	_____	_____
Falter	_____	_____	_____
Cynic	_____	_____	_____

Synonyms Word Search: Locate the target words practiced in this lesson along with their synonyms. Next, pair each target word with its corresponding synonym.

```
V G A O F D C C V H C I N Y C
A N N U X M E Y E G Y D T J D
A F I Z D N Q S G T S O I I B
T F G A S A I K V S Y P S F A
N N F U R T C S K E P T I C L
E E R I A T F I R S I V C L C
L E M T L Z S F O N F E F R N
A N E I W I A N G U D C I D D
V E O P N L A U O E S T W H L
E V I M T E I T C C I H F I O
R R E E M S N R I C H K M M B
P E R H H O E T I O T I M I L
Z T A E D T C S O M N V M U Q
Y N D U N S M W Y I V A Y J D
K I E I N O I T A I C O S S A
```

AFFILIATION	ASSOCIATION	AUDACIOUS
BOLD	CENSURE	COMMON
CONSTRAIN	CRITICISM	CYNIC
DISTINGUISHED	EMINENT	FALTER
HESITATE	INTERCEDE	INTERVENE
LIMIT	PREVALENT	SKEPTIC

Synonyms

Prevalent _____   **Audacious** _____   **Intercede** _____

Affiliation _____   **Censure** _____   **Falter** _____

Eminent _____   **Constrain** _____   **Cynic** _____

Congratulations on completing Lesson 8!

Are you ready to put your skills to the test in this thrilling secret agent escape room? You'll have the chance to become an officially certified secret agent by cracking codes and solving puzzles. Head to the link below or scan the code to embark on your mission. **Remember to play the game on your browser or tablet and click on the full-screen icon for the best experience.**

Let the adventure begin!

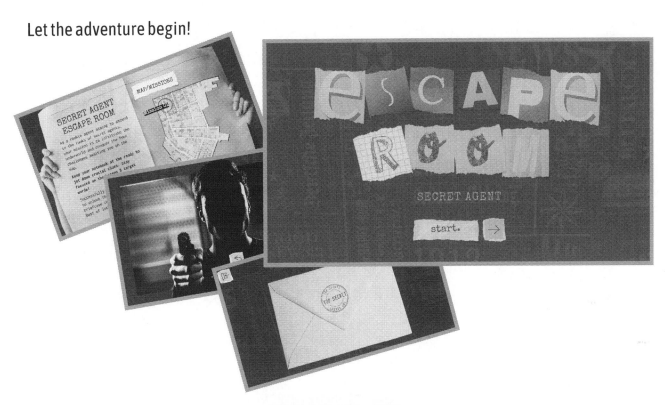

Scan the code on your tablet

or copy this link on your browser:

https://natashascripts.com/secret-agent/

Password to enter: TopSecret8

1. Reflect on your understanding of the words practiced in lesson 8. Can you define each word accurately?

Prevalent:

Affiliation:

Eminent:

Audacious:

Censure:

Constrain:

Intercede:

Falter:

Cynic:
----

2. Can you give an example of something that is prevalent in our society today?

----

3. Have you ever been a part of an organization or group? Describe your affiliation with it.

----

4. Describe a situation where you felt constrained by rules or limitations.

----

5. Can you think of a time when you felt like you were faltering in achieving a goal?

----

6. Do you consider yourself a cynic or an optimist? Why?

Here are the words you'll be learning in the next lesson:

Dearth, Condemn, Deplore, Hackneyed, Exhaustive, Efficacy, Rationale, Aesthetic, Deductive.

Remember:
- Define Objectives: understand meanings, use in sentences, improve spelling.
- Plan Your Learning Approach: flashcards, write sentences, practice daily, use words in conversations.
- Measure Your Success:
  - Spell all words correctly.
  - Successfully use each word in a sentence.

Word	My Goal	My Strategy	Deadline

Lesson 9

Remember: Read with purpose
- pause at each target word,
- review its definition, and then
- continue.

The Housing Affordability Crisis

In contemporary society, there has been a growing concern over the **dearth** of affordable housing options in urban areas. Many **deplore** the current state of housing affordability, citing it as a significant social issue. The **rationale** behind this concern stems from various factors, including rising property prices, and stagnant wage growth. Community leaders and policymakers have been urged to address this issue promptly, with some even **condemning** the **inefficacy** of existing housing policies in addressing the problem. Efforts to improve housing affordability have become a key priority for many cities, highlighting the importance of finding innovative solutions to this pressing issue.

Target Word Definitions

Dearth: A scarcity or lack of something.

Deplore: To strongly disapprove of or regret.

Rationale: The underlying reason or explanation for something.

Condemn: To express strong disapproval or criticism.

Efficacy: The ability of something to produce the desired result or effect.

Inefficacy: The lack of effectiveness or ability to produce the desired result.

List any other words from the passage you want to practice for meaning or spelling.

Spelling

Definition

✏ Break down the words into syllables.

→   →

Dearth	dearth*	_____	_____
Deplore	de - plore	_____	_____
Rationale	ra - tion - ale	_____	_____
Condemn	con - demn	_____	_____
Efficacy	ef - fi - ca - cy	_____	_____

*one syllable

✏ Now write each word in full.

Dearth	_____	_____	_____
Deplore	_____	_____	_____
Rationale	_____	_____	_____
Condemn	_____	_____	_____
Efficacy	_____	_____	_____

✏ My List of Words

_____   _____   _____

_____   _____   _____

_____   _____   _____

_____   _____   _____

Start by reading the definitions of the target words. Then, fill each sentence with the appropriate word. Use each word in two different sentences.

Hackneyed: Something that lacks originality because it has been excessively repeated or overused.
Exhaustive: Thorough and comprehensive, covering all possible details or aspects.
Aesthetic: Concerned with beauty or the appreciation of beauty, particularly in art or design.
Deductive: Figuring things out by using reasoning and proving ideas based on logical thinking.

1. Sir Isaac Newton applied _____ reasoning when he observed an apple falling from a tree, concluding that the force responsible for the apple's fall must also be the same force that keeps the planets in space.

2. The _____ phrase "thinking outside the box" has become so overused that its originality and impact have been diluted.

3. The _____ appeal of the artwork lies in its vibrant colors and harmonious composition, creating a sense of visual pleasure for the viewer.

4. The development of vaccines for novel viruses has necessitated _____ scientific investigations, ensuring their safety and efficacy through rigorous testing and analysis.

5. Despite its _____ plot, the movie was a hit among teenagers who enjoyed the familiar themes and predictable ending.

6. In our English class, we used _____ reasoning to figure out the murderer's identity before the final chapter of the mystery novel.

7. The modern _____ of the new library, with its glass walls and minimalist design, really stands out in our historic neighborhood.

8. After an _____ search for the perfect prom dress, she finally found one that matched her style perfectly.

Break down the words into syllables.

→   →

Hackneyed   hack - neyed   _____   _____

Exhaustive ex - haus - tive _____   _____

Aesthetic   aes - thet - ic   _____   _____

Deductive   de - duc - tive   _____   _____

Now write each word in full.

→   →

Hackneyed   _____   _____   _____

Exhaustive _____   _____   _____

Aesthetic   _____   _____   _____

Deductive   _____   _____   _____

Image Captioning

 Identify the word that best captures the essence of the situation depicted in the image and incorporate it into a sentence that accurately reflects the context of the picture.

Example:

Liquid water on Mars is scarce.

The dearth of liquid water on Mars poses significant challenges for potential human colonization.

Strong Disapproval

_____

_____

_____

_____

Structural Beauty

Reasoning to a Conclusion

Thorough Research

Congratulations on completing Lesson 9!

Are you ready to take a trip to the ancient sands of Egypt and descend into a pyramid to uncover its mysteries? Your adventure into the past starts now, in the labyrinthine corridors and hidden chambers of "The Secret of the Hidden Tomb".

As a daring explorer, you will navigate through puzzles, solve riddles and decipher clues. This is no ordinary journey—you're on a quest to unlock secrets that have been sealed away for millennia in the heart of Egypt!

Let the exploration begin!

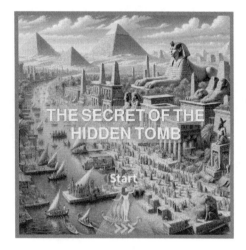  

Scan the code on your tablet

or copy this link on your browser:

https://natashascripts.com/the-hidden-tomb/

Password to enter: HiddenTomb9

Let's review the words practiced in this lesson and reflect on your confidence in spelling and using the words correctly. Below is a table to guide your self-reflection and self-assessment. Rate your confidence on a scale of 1 to 5, where 1 indicates the least confidence and 5 the most. Then list the words you believe need more practice.

List of Words Practiced	How confident do I feel about spelling each word correctly?	How confident do I feel about using each word in a sentence correctly?	Which words do I need to practice more?
dearth	○ ○ ○ ○ ○	○ ○ ○ ○ ○	
condemn	○ ○ ○ ○ ○	○ ○ ○ ○ ○	
deplore	○ ○ ○ ○ ○	○ ○ ○ ○ ○	
hackneyed	○ ○ ○ ○ ○	○ ○ ○ ○ ○	
exhaustive	○ ○ ○ ○ ○	○ ○ ○ ○ ○	
efficacy	○ ○ ○ ○ ○	○ ○ ○ ○ ○	
rationale	○ ○ ○ ○ ○	○ ○ ○ ○ ○	
aesthetic	○ ○ ○ ○ ○	○ ○ ○ ○ ○	
deductive	○ ○ ○ ○ ○	○ ○ ○ ○ ○	
My List of Words			
	○ ○ ○ ○ ○	○ ○ ○ ○ ○	
	○ ○ ○ ○ ○	○ ○ ○ ○ ○	
	○ ○ ○ ○ ○	○ ○ ○ ○ ○	
	○ ○ ○ ○ ○	○ ○ ○ ○ ○	

Setting Goals for the Upcoming Lesson

Here are the words you'll be learning in the next lesson:

Hypothetical, Dichotomy, Debase, Reconcile, Candid, Gregarious, Guile, Exhilarate, Foreshadow.

> Remember:
> - Define Objectives: understand meanings, use in sentences, improve spelling.
> - Plan Your Learning Approach: flashcards, write sentences, practice daily, use words in conversations.
> - Measure Your Success:
>   - Spell all words correctly.
>   - Successfully use each word in a sentence.

Word	My Goal	My Strategy	Deadline

Lesson 10

Read the paragraph to see the target words used in context. Then, read the simplified version of the text which explains the target words. Proceed with the multiple-choice exercise.

Balancing Act

In environmental policy discussions, there exists a **hypothetical** scenario regarding the **dichotomy** between economic development and ecological preservation. Policymakers often face the challenge of balancing these conflicting interests, fearing that prioritizing one could **debase** the other. However, forward-thinking strategies aim to reconcile these opposing forces by fostering sustainable practices that promote both prosperity and environmental health. Recent advancements in renewable energy **foreshadow** a future where such a balance is not only achievable but also advantageous for society and the planet.

Simplified Version: Balancing Act

*In environmental policy discussions, there's a **supposed** situation where people have to choose between the **opposing** goals of making money and taking care of nature. Leaders struggle to find a good balance because they worry that focusing too much on one thing will **harm** the other. But some smart plans try to bring these two ideas together, so we can have both money and a healthy environment. New ways of making energy from things like sunlight and wind **suggest** that we can have both in the future.*

1. What does the term 'hypothetical' imply in the context of environmental policy discussions?

A) A situation based on real events

B) A theoretical or imagined scenario

C) A past occurrence

D) A universally accepted truth

2. What is meant by the 'dichotomy' mentioned in the discussions?

A) The division between national and international policies

B) The contrast between historical and modern practices

C) The split between economic development and ecological preservation

D) The difference in opinions among scientists and policymakers

3. In the paragraph, what does 'debase' suggest about the impact of prioritizing one interest over another?

A) Enhance its importance

B) Broaden its appeal

C) Shift its focus

D) Reduce its value or quality

4. According to the paragraph, how do 'forward-thinking strategies' aim to address environmental issues?

A) By reconciling economic growth with environmental health through sustainable practices

B) By choosing economic development over ecological preservation

C) By focusing solely on advancing technology

D) By eliminating traditional energy sources entirely

5. What does 'foreshadow' indicate about recent advancements in renewable energy?

A) They predict difficulties in achieving a balance between development and preservation

B) They suggest a decline in technological innovation

C) They hint at a future where balance between economic and ecological interests is beneficial

D) They show a shift away from renewable resources

Now read the Target Word Analysis on the next page and complete the spelling practice activities.

Target Word Analysis

Hypothetical: This refers to a situation that is imagined or supposed, rather than real or factual. In the paragraph, it describes a made-up situation where people have to make a choice between two options.

Dichotomy: This means there's a clear division or contrast between two things, in this case, between making money and protecting the environment. The phrase highlights the idea that these two goals might seem opposed to each other.

Debase: This means to reduce the quality or value of something. In the paragraph, it suggests that focusing too much on one goal could harm or lower the quality of the other goal. For example, if economic development takes precedence over ecological preservation, it could harm the environment.

Foreshadow: This means to give a hint or indication of what might happen in the future. In the context of the paragraph, it suggests that the current actions or plans could indicate what the future will be like, specifically a future where both economic development and ecological preservation are possible.

Observation: Look closely at each target word below. Circle any letters you find tricky to remember.

Hypothetical   Dichotomy

Debase   Foreshadow

Break down the words into syllables.

	$\longrightarrow$		$\longrightarrow$
Hypothetical	**hy - po - thet - i - cal**	_____	_____
Dichotomy	**di - chot - o - my**	_____	_____
Debase	**de - base**	_____	_____
Foreshadow	**fore - shad - ow**	_____	_____
		_____	_____

✎ **Now write each word in full.**

Hypothetical _____ _____ _____

Dichotomy _____ _____ _____

Debase _____ _____ _____

Foreshadow _____ _____ _____

✎

Start by reading the definitions of the target words. Then, fill each sentence with the appropriate word.

Reconcile: To restore a friendship or settle a dispute.
Candid: Open and honest.
Gregarious: Sociable and fond of company.
Guile: Sly or cunning intelligence, often used in deceitful ways.
Exhilarate: To make (someone) feel very happy, animated or elated.

1. The _____ feeling of freedom filled Becka's heart as she stood on the mountaintop, soaking in the breathtaking view.

2. Despite his charming demeanor, Jack's _____ often led him to trouble as he schemed his way out of difficult situations.

3. The politician's _____ remarks about the state of the economy sparked a lively debate among the audience.

4. After their heated argument, Camille found it challenging to _____ with her best friend, but eventually, they managed to mend their friendship.

5. Known for his _____ nature, Burn easily strikes up conversations with strangers and makes friends wherever he goes.

✏️ **Break down the words into syllables.**

		→	
Reconcile	rec - on - cile	_____	_____
Candid	can - did	_____	_____
Gregarious	gre - gar - i - ous	_____	_____
Guile	guile	_____	_____
Exhilarating	ex - hil - a - rat - ing	_____	_____

✏️

Observation: Look closely at each target word below. Circle any letters you find tricky to remember.

Reconcile   Candid   Guile
Gregarious Exhilarating

Remember:
- **Spot Tricky Letters**
- **Focus Your Efforts**
- **Develop Strategies**

✏️ **Now write each word in full.**

Reconcile	_____	_____	_____
Candid	_____	_____	_____
Gregarious	_____	_____	_____
Guile	_____	_____	_____
Exhilarating	_____	_____	_____
Hypothetical	_____	_____	_____
Dichotomy	_____	_____	_____
Debase	_____	_____	_____
Foreshadow	_____	_____	_____

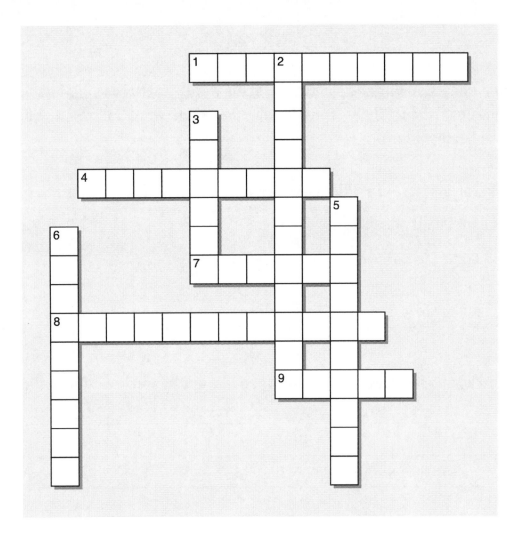

Across

1. When spooky music starts playing, it's a sign that ghosts are near!

4. Repair a friendship rift with a hug and a heartfelt apology

7. Turning a superhero into a bumbling sidekick – the ultimate humiliation!

8. Imagine a world where aliens walk among us – it's this kind of story!

9. Sneaky like a fox, using tricks to outsmart others.

Down

2. Skydiving or rollercoaster rides, they're this kind of thrilling!

3. Spill the tea without holding back, like a celebrity on a talk show.

5. Life of the party, always ready for a group selfie.

6. Like choosing between pizza and ice cream – the tough choice of life!

Hypothetical, Dichotomy, Debase, Reconcile, Candid, Gregarious, Guile, Exhilarate, Foreshadow.

Reflect on your understanding and application of the words practiced in this lesson. Answer the following questions thoughtfully, considering how each word relates to your personal experiences and observations.

Can you provide an example of a situation where you might need to reconcile differences between friends or family members?

_____

_____

_____

Describe a time when you were praised for being candid and honest in a difficult situation.

_____

_____

_____

How do you feel in social settings – are you more gregarious and outgoing, or do you prefer quiet and solitude?

_____

_____

_____

Have you ever encountered someone who used guile or cunning to achieve their goals? How did you handle the situation?

_____

_____

Think of an experience that was truly exhilarating for you – what made it so thrilling?

_____

_____

_____

Do you see a dichotomy between studying for exams and participating in extracurricular activities? How do you balance both?

_____

_____

_____

Can you identify any events in history that seemed to foreshadow future developments or outcomes?

_____

_____

_____

Have you ever witnessed someone trying to debase another person's reputation? How did it make you feel?

_____

_____

_____

Can you imagine a hypothetical scenario where humans have colonized Mars? What challenges do you think they might face?

_____

_____

_____

Here are the words you'll be learning in the next lesson:

Escalate, Declamation, Coerce, Squander, Equivocal, Magnitude, Loquacious, Foreseeable, Judicious.

Remember:
- Define Objectives: understand meanings, use in sentences, improve spelling.
- Plan Your Learning Approach: flashcards, write sentences, practice daily, use words in conversations.
- Measure Your Success:
  - Spell all words correctly.
  - Successfully use each word in a sentence.

Word	My Goal	My Strategy	Deadline

Lesson 11

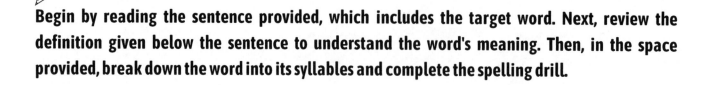

Begin by reading the sentence provided, which includes the target word. Next, review the definition given below the sentence to understand the word's meaning. Then, in the space provided, break down the word into its syllables and complete the spelling drill.

---

1. The argument between the two friends began to **escalate** when neither was willing to back down.

Definition of "Escalate" : To increase rapidly or intensify, especially in a conflict or situation.

es - ca - late ⟶ _____ _____ _____

escalate ⟶ _____ _____ _____

---

2. The student delivered a powerful **declamation** about the importance of environmental conservation to the school assembly.

Definition of "Declamation": A formal or passionate speech or delivery, often practiced or rehearsed.

dec - la - ma - tion ⟶ _____ _____ _____

declamation ⟶ _____ _____ _____

3. Despite being warned about the importance of saving money, she continued to **squander** her allowance on unnecessary items.

Definition of "Squander": To waste recklessly or extravagantly, often resources like time, money, or opportunities.
squan - der   ⟶   _____   _____   _____
squander   ⟶   _____   _____   _____

4. The politician's **equivocal** response to the journalist's question left many unsure of where they stood on the issue.

Definition of "Equivocal": Open to more than one interpretation, ambiguous or unclear in meaning.
e - quiv - o - cal   ⟶   _____   _____   _____
equivocal   ⟶   _____   _____   _____

5. The **magnitude** of the earthquake was so great that it could be felt hundreds of miles away.

Definition of "Magnitude": The great size or importance of something.
mag - ni - tude   ⟶   _____   _____   _____
magnitude   ⟶   _____   _____   _____

6. Sarah's **loquacious** nature made her a favorite among her classmates, as she always had interesting stories to share.

Definition of "Loquacious": Very talkative or chatty.

lo - qua - cious →	_____ _____ _____
loquacious →	_____ _____ _____

7. It was **foreseeable** that skipping class would result in detention, yet he chose to do it anyway.

Definition of "Foreseeable": Expected to happen or occur in the future.

fore - see - able →	_____ _____ _____
foreseeable →	_____ _____ _____

8. The teacher made a **judicious** decision to postpone the test until after the class had more time to study.

Definition of "Judicious": Showing good judgment or wisdom in decision-making.

ju - di -cious →	_____ _____ _____
judicious →	_____ _____ _____

9. The bully tried to **coerce** the younger students into giving him their lunch money by threatening them.

Definition of "Coerce": To persuade or force someone to do something through threats, intimidation, or pressure.
co - erce $\longrightarrow$ _____ _____ _____
coerce $\longrightarrow$ _____ _____ _____

Target Words

Escalate, Declamation, Coerce, Squander, Equivocal, Magnitude, Loquacious, Foreseeable, Judicious.

Review the definitions of the target words. Then, fill each sentence with the appropriate word.

1. The dictator attempted to _____ the citizens into submission through fear and intimidation.

2. Given the current economic trends, a recession seemed _____ to many financial analysts.

3. During the annual _____ contest, Carey captivated the audience with her impassioned recital of the poem she wrote.

4. The judge made a _____ decision based on careful consideration of all the evidence presented in court.

5. Rebeka is known for being _____, often dominating conversations with her endless stories and anecdotes.

6. As tensions continued to _____ between the two rival companies, the need for a skilled mediator became increasingly apparent.

Observation: Look closely at each target word below. Circle any letters you find tricky to remember.

Escalate

Declamation

Coerce

Squander

Magnitude

Equivocal

Foreseeable

Loquacious

Judicious

Match each synonym with its corresponding word.

Predictable   Escalate

Force   Declamation

Speech   Coerce

Wise   Squander

Intensify   Equivocal

Waste   Magnitude

Chatty   Loquacious

Size   Foreseeable

Ambiguous   Judicious

Word Match

Match each situation with the word that best describes it.

Target Words

Escalate

Declamation

Coerce

Squander

Equivocal

Magnitude

Loquacious

Foreseeable

Judicious

1. A person tries to convince someone else to do something they don't want to by using threats or manipulation.

_____

2. A lottery winner quickly spends all of their prize money on expensive cars, vacations, and luxury items.

_____

3. Two countries are in a dispute over a border. One country sends more troops to the area, leading to increased tension.

_____

4. Weather forecasters predict a major snowstorm based on the gathering clouds and dropping temperatures.

_____

5. An activist delivers a passionate speech in front of a large crowd, advocating for social change.

_____

6. A manager gives a vague and ambiguous response to an employee's question, avoiding providing clear guidance.

_____

7. A chef meticulously selects the finest ingredients and prepares a delicious and balanced meal.

_____

8. During a town hall meeting, one attendee dominates the discussion, speaking at length and interrupting others.

_____

9. A hurricane with powerful winds and torrential rain strikes a coastal town, causing extensive damage and flooding.

_____

Target Words

Escalate

Declamation

Coerce

Squander

Equivocal

Magnitude

Loquacious

Foreseeable

Judicious

✏ **Reflective Writing: Write a reflective response to the following prompts using your own experiences, examples and observations to support your answers. Here's an example:**

Reflect on a time when you had to make a judicious decision. What factors did you consider and how did you ultimately reach your conclusion.

Last year, I had to decide between joining the school band or taking an advanced placement course. I considered my passion for music, academic goals, and future career in engineering. After discussing it with my parents and teachers, I chose the advanced placement course to better align with my long-term objectives. It was a hard decision, but I believe it was the right one for my future.

1. Reflect on a time when you had to make a **judicious** decision. What factors did you consider, and how did you ultimately reach your conclusion?

_____

_____

_____

_____

2. Describe a situation where you encountered someone who was **loquacious**. How did you handle the conversation, and what did you learn from the experience?

_____

_____

_____

_____

3. Have you ever been in a situation where it was **foreseeable** that something would happen? How did you prepare for it, and what was the outcome?

_____

_____

_____

_____

Congratulations on completing Lesson 11!

Are you prepared to unravel a murder mystery aboard the Orient Waves, a luxurious cruise liner that journeyed across the East China Sea in 1931?

As Detective Lockerby's assistant, you'll play a crucial role in solving the murder of Lady Evelyn, a distinguished socialite with extensive estates in Great Britain. Together with the detective, you'll evaluate clues and complete quizzes to ultimately reveal the truth behind Lady Evelyn's untimely demise.

Proceed to the "Murder Mystery" game and embark on your investigative journey!

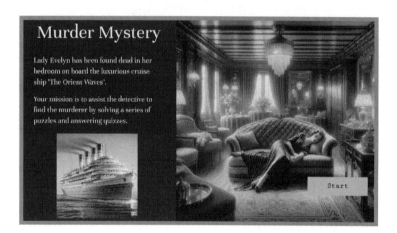

Scan the code on your tablet

or copy this link on your browser:

https://natashascripts.com/murder-mystery/

Password to enter: OrientWaves11

Let's review the words practiced in this lesson and reflect on your confidence in spelling and using the words correctly. Below is a table to guide your self-reflection and self-assessment. Rate your confidence on a scale of 1 to 5, where 1 indicates the least confidence and 5 the most. Then list the words you believe need more practice.

List of Words Practiced	How confident do I feel about spelling each word correctly?	How confident do I feel about using each word in a sentence correctly?	Which words do I need to practice more?
escalate	○ ○ ○ ○ ○	○ ○ ○ ○ ○	
declamation	○ ○ ○ ○ ○	○ ○ ○ ○ ○	
coerce	○ ○ ○ ○ ○	○ ○ ○ ○ ○	
squander	○ ○ ○ ○ ○	○ ○ ○ ○ ○	
equivocal	○ ○ ○ ○ ○	○ ○ ○ ○ ○	
magnitude	○ ○ ○ ○ ○	○ ○ ○ ○ ○	
loquacious	○ ○ ○ ○ ○	○ ○ ○ ○ ○	
foreseeable	○ ○ ○ ○ ○	○ ○ ○ ○ ○	
judicious	○ ○ ○ ○ ○	○ ○ ○ ○ ○	

Here are the words you'll be learning in the next lesson:

Tirade, Advocate, Vexation, Palpable, Pseudonym, Contrive, Cognizant, Ubiquity, Dissenting, Constructive.

Remember:
- Define Objectives: understand meanings, use in sentences, improve spelling.
- Plan Your Learning Approach: flashcards, write sentences, practice daily, use words in conversations.
- Measure Your Success:
  - Spell all words correctly.
  - Successfully use each word in a sentence.

Word	My Goal	My Strategy	Deadline

Lesson 12

Read the passage. Then, answer the questions that follow.

Social Media Outburst

As the clock struck midnight, Madison's phone buzzed with a notification. Curious, she unlocked her screen to find herself tagged in a heated debate on social media. A tirade of angry comments flooded the thread, directed at her recent blog post advocating for the notion that taxes paid to accommodate undocumented immigrants were not badly spent.

Madison's heart sank as she read through the comments, each one more vicious than the last. The vexation she felt was palpable, knowing that her well-intentioned words had sparked such outrage. Despite her attempts to remain calm, the relentless barrage of negativity gnawed at her resolve.

With each new comment, Madison's frustration grew. It seemed that no amount of reasoning could quell the anger of those determined to oppose her views. Contingent upon her hopes for meaningful dialogue, she had never expected such vitriol in response.

Desperate to shield herself from the onslaught, Madison briefly considered adopting a pseudonym to escape the backlash. However, her commitment to transparency prevailed, and she resolved to face the criticism head-on, even as it threatened to overwhelm her.

In the midst of the chaos, Madison contrived a plan to turn the tide of the conversation. She typed a carefully thought response, addressing the concerns raised by her critics. Though the task was daunting, she remained cognizant of the importance of standing up for what she believed in.

Despite the ubiquity of negativity online, Madison refused to be silenced. With each word she typed, she hoped to foster understanding and empathy in a digital landscape fraught with division. Her thorough approach to engaging with dissenting voices spoke volumes about her resilience in the face of adversity.

As the night wore on, Madison's efforts bore fruit. The tone of the conversation shifted, with some participants expressing appreciation for her willingness to engage constructively. Though the scars of the ordeal remained, Emily emerged stronger, reaffirming her commitment to using social media as a platform for positive change.

Answer the following questions. Try to complete the activity on your own first. If you find it absolutely necessary, refer to the Word List and Definitions section for clarification on any words on page 243

1. Which word evidences that there were many angry comments?

_____

2. What does the term 'advocating' mean in the context of the narrative?

    A) Ignoring the concerns of others in favor of one's own opinions.

    B) Publicly supporting or recommending a particular cause or policy.

    C) Making a financial contribution to a cause.

3. What emotions does she experience as she reads through the comments?

    A) Excitement and anticipation

    B) Indifference and boredom

    C) Frustration and despair

Write down the word that evidences this. _____

4. Why does Madison decide not to use a pseudonym to answer the angry comments?

_____

_____

_____

5. What qualities does Madison demonstrate in her response to the critics?

_____

_____

6. What does the phrase "Despite the ubiquity of negativity online" mean?

    A) Despite the prevalence

    B) Despite the occurrence

    C) Despite the incidence

7. Reflecting on Madison's experience, discuss the challenges and benefits of engaging in online debates about controversial topics.

_____

_____

_____

_____

_____

_____

_____

8. Consider Madison's decision to address the criticism directly instead of avoiding it. Do you think this was the right approach? Why or why not?

_____

_____

_____

_____

_____

_____

_____

Refer to page 234 for examples of valid answers.

Read the sentence provided, which includes the target word. Next, review the definition given below the sentence. Then, in the space provided, break down the word into its syllables and complete the spelling drill.

1. During the team meeting, the coach launched into a **tirade** about the importance of teamwork and discipline after noticing the lackluster performance in the last game.

Definition of "Tirade": A long, angry speech or series of complaints about something.

ti - rade ⟶ _____ _____ _____

tirade ⟶ _____ _____ _____

2. The 10th graders spent the afternoon **advocating** for environmental protection by organizing a community cleanup and educating their peers on recycling practices.

Definition of "Advocating": Actively supporting or recommending a particular cause or policy.

ad - vo - cat - ing ⟶ _____ _____ _____

advocating ⟶ _____ _____ _____

3. The constant noise from the construction site was a source of **vexation** for the students trying to study in the nearby library.

Definition of "Vexation" : A state of being annoyed, frustrated, or worried.

vex - a - tion ⟶ _____ _____ _____

vexation ⟶ _____ _____ _____

4. The excitement in the room was **palpable** as the students awaited the announcement of the competition winner.

Definition of "Palpable": So intense as to be almost touched or felt.

pal - pa - ble ⟶ _____ _____ _____

palpable ⟶ _____ _____ _____

5. To protect his anonymity, the whistleblower reported the misconduct under the **pseudonym** "John Doe".

Definition of "Pseudonym" : A fictitious name used by an author to conceal their identity.

pseu - do - nym ⟶ _____ _____ _____

pseudonym ⟶ _____ _____ _____

Read the definitions of the target words. Then complete the syllabification of each word and fill in the blank using the appropriate word. Each word will be used twice, so be sure to fill in two different sentences for each word.

Contrive: To plan with ingenuity or to invent.			
con - trive ⟶	_____	_____	_____
Ubiquity: The state of being everywhere all at once or seeming to be everywhere at the same time.			
u - biq - ui - ty ⟶	_____	_____	_____
Dissent: Disagreement with the majority opinion.			
dis - sent ⟶	_____	_____	_____
Constructive: Serving a useful purpose or tending to build up or improve.			
con - struc - tive ⟶	_____	_____	_____
Target Words: Contrive, Ubiquity, Dissent, Constructive.			

1. The _____ of smartphones has dramatically changed how we communicate and access information.

2. The teacher's _____ feedback helped students improve their essays significantly.

3. In the council vote, her voice was the only _____ against the proposed development plan.

4. She managed to _____ a meeting between the two rivals, hoping they would reconcile.

5. Walking through the art exhibit, the _____ of abstract paintings, present at every turn, highlighted the popular trend among contemporary artists.

6. To win the science fair, Julia had to _____ a device that could clean water using only sunlight, demonstrating her ability to invent clever solutions.

7. Faced with the decision to adopt a new school uniform, Ana's _____ stood out as she argued for individual expression, sparking a wider conversation about personal freedom versus collective identity.

8. In the woodworking workshop, the instructor's _____ advice helped students understand not just what mistakes they made, but how to correct them

Image Interpretation

Each image below represents a word we've practiced in this lesson. Examine the images closely and identify which word each one expresses.

Let's review the words practiced in this lesson and reflect on your confidence in spelling and using the words correctly. Below is a table to guide your self-reflection and self-assessment. Rate your confidence on a scale of 1 to 5, where 1 indicates the least confidence and 5 the most. Then list the words you believe need more practice.

List of Words Practiced	How confident do I feel about spelling each word correctly?	How confident do I feel about using each word in a sentence correctly?	Which words do I need to practice more?
tirade	○ ○ ○ ○ ○	○ ○ ○ ○ ○	
advocate	○ ○ ○ ○ ○	○ ○ ○ ○ ○	
vexation	○ ○ ○ ○ ○	○ ○ ○ ○ ○	
palpable	○ ○ ○ ○ ○	○ ○ ○ ○ ○	
pseudonym	○ ○ ○ ○ ○	○ ○ ○ ○ ○	
contrive	○ ○ ○ ○ ○	○ ○ ○ ○ ○	
ubiquity	○ ○ ○ ○ ○	○ ○ ○ ○ ○	
dissent	○ ○ ○ ○ ○	○ ○ ○ ○ ○	
constructive	○ ○ ○ ○ ○	○ ○ ○ ○ ○	

Review the words from Lessons 10-12 and then take a fun break from the workbook and prepare for an exciting adventure in our next lesson: the online escape room "The Lost City of Atlantis".

Lesson 13

Congratulations on finishing lessons 10-12!

Are you ready to embark on an extraordinary journey to uncover the secrets of the lost city of Atlantis?

This interactive game is designed as a quest, consisting of two challenging quizzes that will test your spelling skills and word usage practiced in lessons 10-12. Successfully complete these quizzes, and you will play a pivotal role in reviving the legendary Atlantis! Your journey doesn't end there—after completing the main challenges, you'll have the opportunity to provide feedback through a final quiz, ensuring your adventure is not only educational but also rewarding. Dive into history, unravel mysteries, and restore the glory of Atlantis. Are you up for the challenge?

Scan the code on your tablet

or copy this link on your browser:
https://sites.google.com/view/thelostcityofatlantis/home

No Password Required

Here are the words you'll be learning in the next lesson:

Explicit, Infuriate, Conducive, Sabotage, Deviate, Exonerate, Lyrical, Profound, Elation.

Remember:
- Define Objectives: understand meanings, use in sentences, improve spelling.
- Plan Your Learning Approach: flashcards, write sentences, practice daily, use words in conversations.
- Measure Your Success:
  - Spell all words correctly.
  - Successfully use each word in a sentence.

Word	My Goal	My Strategy	Deadline

Lesson 14

In this activity, you'll explore the use of a specific word across different contexts and expressions. You'll first identify its meaning through context, then apply it in a sentence, and finally, practice its spelling. If you find it absolutely necessary, refer to the Word List and Definitions section for clarification on any words on page 243. This exercise aims to deepen your understanding of the word's usage and enhance your writing skills.

Explicit

1. In the meeting, the CEO was **explicit** about the company's zero-tolerance policy towards any form of harassment, ensuring all employees understood the consequences.

2. The software developer added comments to the code to make the function's purpose more **explicit**, helping future maintainers understand its intricacies.

3. While browsing the library, she found an old map with **explicit** details of the old coastal area, which included handwritten notes by the explorer.

1. What does the word "explicit" mean as used in the sentences above?
A. Involving detailed and comprehensive information
B. Clearly and directly expressed, with no ambiguity
C. Expressed in a complicated manner
D. Suggested but not plainly expressed

Complete the following sentence starters by incorporating the word "explicit" to clearly convey the intended meaning.

2. The teacher's instructions for the assignment were unequivocal, ensuring that every student understood what was required.

To ensure no confusion, _____

_____

3. He gave me direct feedback on my presentation, pointing out exactly what needed improvement without any ambiguity.

During the review, his _____

_____

4. The contract had **explicit** terms and conditions, which helped avoid any potential misunderstandings between the parties involved.

To prevent any disputes, _____

_____

Infuriate

1. The unfair decision by the referee **infuriated** the players, who argued vehemently against the call.
2. Sarah's little brother knew exactly how to **infuriate** her by messing up her room right after she had cleaned it.
3. The constant delays on the project timeline began to **infuriate** the team, leading to increased tension among the employees.

5. What does the word "infuriate" mean as used in the sentences above?
A) To confuse thoroughly.
B) To cause to feel mild annoyance.
C) To make extremely angry.
D) To disappoint deeply.

Complete the following sentence starters by incorporating the word "infuriate" to clearly convey the intended meaning.

6. The unjust ruling by the judge enraged the community activists.

The community activists _____

_____

7. His continual procrastination exasperated his project partner.

His project partner was _____

_____

8. The mocking tone in his voice angered her.

She was _____

_____

Conducive

1. The quiet library atmosphere is **conducive** to studying for hours without interruption.
2. Their teacher created a **conducive** environment in the classroom that encouraged open discussions and collaborative learning.
3. Proper hydration and regular breaks during practice are **conducive** to optimal athletic performance.

9. What does the word "conducive" mean in the context of the sentences provided?

A) Demanding significant effort or attention.
B) Existing in a state of comfort and stability.
C) Contributing positively or helping to bring about.
D) Related to conducting official tasks or duties.

Read the following sentences and rewrite them by incorporating the word "conducive". Ensure that the revised sentences maintain their original meaning.

10. The peaceful setting of the garden is ideal for meditation and reflection.

----

11. The coach's supportive approach promotes a positive environment for team growth.

----

12. Having a dedicated workspace at home is beneficial for maintaining productivity during remote work.

Sabotage

1. Deliberately leaving out important information from the report was an act of **sabotage** against the organization.

2. Spreading rumors to undermine a colleague's reputation is a clear example of workplace **sabotage**.

3. Hacking into the company's database to alter information is considered to be **sabotage** and has legal consequences.

13. What does the word "sabotage" mean as used in the sentences above?

A) To support and promote efficiency.

B) To destroy or obstruct something for advantage.

C) To accidentally cause a malfunction in a process.

D) To repair or fix an issue discreetly.

The following words are synonyms of "sabotage":

Undermine	Subvert	Disrupt

Fill each sentence with the appropriate word.

14. She was accused of _____ the campaign by leaking confidential strategies to competitors.

15. _____ the team's efforts by withholding key resources led to project failure..

16. _____ the assembly line process intentionally caused significant production delays

Deviate

1. The pilot had to **deviate** from the planned route due to unexpected bad weather.

2. It's important not to **deviate** from the guidelines given in the experiment to ensure accurate results.

3. During the debate, he tried hard not to **deviate** from the main topic despite various provocations.

17. What does the word "deviate" mean as used in the sentences above?

A) To follow a set path closely.

B) To stray or depart from a standard, norm, or topic.

C) To accelerate towards a goal.

D) To enhance the effectiveness of a plan.

The following words are synonyms of "deviate":

Diverge	Stray	Veer

Rewrite the following sentences, replacing "deviate" with the synonyms provided above. Assign each synonym to a different sentence:

18. The board of directors **deviated** from the scheduled agenda, causing the meeting to extend by two hours.

----

19. During his presentation, he **deviated** from the topic, which caused confusion among the audience.

----

20. She had to **deviate** from her usual routine to accommodate the new project.

✏ **Break down the words into syllables.**

⟶ ⟶

Explicit	ex - plic - it	_____	_____
Infuriate	in - fu - ri - ate	_____	_____
Conducive	con - du - cive	_____	_____
Sabotage	sab - o - tage	_____	_____
Deviate	de - vi - ate	_____	_____

✏ **Now write each word in full.**

⟶ ⟶

Explicit	_____	_____	_____
Infuriate	_____	_____	_____
Conducive	_____	_____	_____
Sabotage	_____	_____	_____
Deviate	_____	_____	_____

Start by reading the definitions of the target words. Then, fill each sentence with the appropriate word. Use each word in two different sentences.

Target Word Definitions

Exonerate: To officially declare someone not guilty of a charge or wrongdoing.

Lyrical: Expressing deep personal emotions or observations, often in a way that is like a song or poem.

Profound: Very deep or intense, whether in terms of thoughts, feelings, or insights; having great significance or impact.

Elation: A state of great happiness and exhilaration.

1. The poet's _____ verses about nature captured the beauty of the changing seasons.

2. The documentary aimed to _____ the misunderstood leader by showing new aspects of their decisions and life.

3. She couldn't hide her _____ when she found out she had won the scholarship to her dream university.

4. Listening to the _____ melody of the violin, she felt a sense of peace she hadn't felt in years.

5. His _____ insight on the subject of artificial intelligence was evident, as he could answer even the most complex questions.

6. The news of the team's victory brought _____ to the entire school, sparking celebrations throughout the campus.

7. After reviewing the new evidence, the judge decided to _____ the accused from all charges.

8. The novel's exploration of love and loss had a _____ impact on her perspective on relationships.

Break down the words into syllables.

		→	→
Exonerate	ex - on - er - ate	_____	_____
Lyrical	lyr - i - cal	_____	_____
Profound	pro - found	_____	_____
Elation	e - la - tion	_____	_____

Now write each word in full.

	→	→
Exonerate	_____	_____	_____
Lyrical	_____	_____	_____
Profound	_____	_____	_____
Elation	_____	_____	_____

Write a short paragraph for each provided prompt using the specified vocabulary words. Ensure each word is correctly applied in context. Example answers for guidance on structuring your responses can be found on page 236.

Explicit, Infuriate, Conducive, Sabotage, Deviate, Exonerate, Lyrical, Profound, Elation.

1. Write a set of explicit instructions on how to prepare your favorite meal so that someone who has never cooked before can follow them easily.

_____

_____

_____

_____

_____

_____

2. Describe an incident that infuriated you. What happened, and how did it escalate to cause such a reaction?

_____

_____

_____

_____

_____

3. Write a short story about a character who tries to win a competition by sabotaging a rival. What was their plan, and what were the consequences of their actions?

_____

_____

_____

_____

_____

_____

4. Write about a time when you or a fictional character deviated from a planned route or decision. What prompted the deviation, and what was the outcome?

_____

_____

_____

_____

_____

_____

_____

5. Write a narrative where the main character is exonerated from a serious accusation. What was the accusation, and how did new evidence come to light?

_____

_____

_____

_____

_____

_____

_____

6. Write a lyrical description of a scene from nature, such as a forest, beach, or mountain. Use vivid imagery and emotional language to bring the scene life.

_____

_____

_____

_____

_____

_____

_____

7. Discuss a profound realization you had about yourself, someone else or the world. How did this insight come about, and how has it influenced your perspective?

_____

_____

_____

_____

_____

_____

_____

8. Describe a moment of elation following a personal achievement or success. What was the achievement, and what made this moment so memorable?

_____

_____

_____

_____

_____

_____

_____

9. Imagine you're designing the ultimate hangout spot for you and your friends. Describe what features make this space conducive to fun, relaxation, and creativity.

_____

_____

_____

_____

_____

Let's review the words practiced in this lesson and reflect on your confidence in spelling and using the words correctly. Below is a table to guide your self-reflection and self-assessment. Rate your confidence on a scale of 1 to 5, where 1 indicates the least confidence and 5 the most. Then list the words you believe need more practice.

List of Words Practiced	How confident do I feel about spelling each word correctly?	How confident do I feel about using each word in a sentence correctly?	Which words do I need to practice more?
Explicit	○ ○ ○ ○ ○	○ ○ ○ ○ ○	
Infuriate	○ ○ ○ ○ ○	○ ○ ○ ○ ○	
Conducive	○ ○ ○ ○ ○	○ ○ ○ ○ ○	
Sabotage	○ ○ ○ ○ ○	○ ○ ○ ○ ○	
Deviate	○ ○ ○ ○ ○	○ ○ ○ ○ ○	
Exonerate	○ ○ ○ ○ ○	○ ○ ○ ○ ○	
Lyrical	○ ○ ○ ○ ○	○ ○ ○ ○ ○	
Profound	○ ○ ○ ○ ○	○ ○ ○ ○ ○	
Elation	○ ○ ○ ○ ○	○ ○ ○ ○ ○	

Here are the words you'll be learning in the next lesson:

Ephemeral, Fascinated, Cumulative, Lucid, Enunciate, Germane, Eccentric, Extraneous.

Remember:
- Define Objectives: understand meanings, use in sentences, improve spelling.
- Plan Your Learning Approach: flashcards, write sentences, practice daily, use words in conversations.
- Measure Your Success:
  - Spell all words correctly.
  - Successfully use each word in a sentence.

Word	My Goal	My Strategy	Deadline

Lesson 15

Remember: Read with purpose
- pause at each target word,
- review its definition, and then
- continue.

Transitory Canvases

In the quirky art room adorned with splashes of color and unconventional sculptures, Ms. Brim's teaching style captivated her students. Known for her **eccentric** approach to art, she fascinated her ninth graders with projects that challenged their creativity and perspective. Today, she emphasized the **ephemeral** beauty of installation art, which exists only briefly before being dismantled. As she **enunciated** each instruction, her students followed with rapt attention. The projects were designed to build on one another, with the **cumulative** effect of producing a new and original integrated form of installation art. Ms. Brim always made sure her lessons were **germane** to contemporary art techniques aiming to inspire her students to think critically and apply their creativity.

Target Word Definitions

Eccentric: Unconventional or unusual.

Ephemeral: Lasting for a very short time.

Enunciate: To pronounce words clearly and distinctly.

Cumulative: Increasing or growing by accumulation or successive additions.

Germane: Relevant to the topic or subject at hand.

List any other words from the passage you want to practice for meaning or spelling.

Spelling   Meaning and Definition

----------------------   --

----------------------   --

----------------------   --

1. What term best describes Ms. Brim's unconventional approach to art?
A) Traditional
B) Unorthodox
C) Mundane
D) Conventional

2. Which word best characterizes the transient nature of installation art?
A) Lasting
B) Enduring
C) Permanent
D) Fleeting

3. How did Ms. Brim ensure her instructions were clearly communicated to her students?
A) Articulated
B) Mumbled
C) Whispered
D) Spoke softly

4. Which term describes installation art as a series of singular projects integrated to form one original art form?
A) Isolated
B) Unified
C) Fragmented
D) Aggregated

5. Which word describes Ms. Brim's aim to ensure her lessons were directly relevant to contemporary art techniques?
A) Joined
B) Pertinent
C) Inapplicable
D) Related

Break down the words into syllables.

Eccentric	ec - cen - tric	_____	_____
Ephemeral	e - phem - eral	_____	_____
Enunciate	e - nun - ci - ate	_____	_____
Cumulative	cu - mu - la - tive	_____	_____
Germane	ger - mane	_____	_____

Now write each word in full.

Eccentric	_____	_____	_____
Ephemeral	_____	_____	_____
Enunciate	_____	_____	_____
Cumulative	_____	_____	_____
Germane	_____	_____	_____

My List of Words

_____   _____   _____

_____   _____   _____

_____   _____   _____

_____   _____   _____

Read the definitions of the target words. Then complete the syllabification of each word and fill in each sentence using the appropriate word. Each word will be used twice, so be sure to fill in two different sentences for each word.

Fascinated: Deeply interested and absorbed by something.		
fas - ci - nat - ed ⟶ _____	_____	_____
Lucid: Clearly expressed ⟶		
lu - cid _____	_____	_____
Extraneous: Not relevant or directly related to the subject at hand. ⟶		
ex - tra - ne - ous _____	_____	_____

Target Words: Fascinated, Lucid, Extraneous.

1. To keep her essay concise, she removed all _____ details that were not directly relevant to her main argument about climate change.

2. Sam was _____ by the complex social structure of ants, spending hours in the garden observing their cooperative behaviors.

3. Ava was _____ by the planet Jupiter, often observing its immense size through her telescope.

4. Jake's explanation of photosynthesis was so _____ that even his younger sister could understand how plants convert sunlight into energy.

5. When Mia visited Japan for the first time, she found the ritual of removing shoes before entering a home completely _____ to her culture.

6. Her _____ presentation on the Civil Rights Movement impressed her classmates, who suggested she consider a career in politics because of her clear and persuasive speaking skills.

1. Reflect on your understanding of the words practiced in this lesson. Can you define each word accurately?

Eccentric: _____

Ephemeral: _____

Enunciate: _____

Cumulative: _____

Germane: _____

Fascinated: _____

Lucid: _____

Extraneous: _____

Example:

Think about an eccentric person you know or have read about. Describe what makes them unusual and how their unique characteristics have influenced you or others around them.

My uncle is the most eccentric person I know because he dresses like he's still living in the 1970s and talks to plants as if they were people. His unusual style and behavior taught me the importance of expressing oneself freely and not worrying about others' opinions.

2. Think about an eccentric person you know or have read about. Describe what makes them unusual and how their unique characteristics have influenced you or others around them.

_____

_____

_____

_____

_____

3. Reflect on an ephemeral moment in your life, such as a brief but memorable event. Describe why this moment stood out to you and what lasting impact it has had on your perspective.

----

4. Discuss how the cumulative knowledge you've gained over this school year in one subject has helped you improve or change your understanding of that subject. Give specific examples of how this knowledge build-up has been beneficial.

----

5. Describe an instance where you had to explain something complex in a lucid manner to someone who was unfamiliar with the topic.

Let's review the words practiced in this lesson and reflect on your confidence in spelling and using the words correctly. Below is a table to guide your self-reflection and self-assessment. Rate your confidence on a scale of 1 to 5, where 1 indicates the least confidence and 5 the most. Then list the words you believe need more practice.

List of Words Practiced	How confident do I feel about spelling each word correctly?	How confident do I feel about using each word in a sentence correctly?	Which words do I need to practice more?
Eccentric	○ ○ ○ ○ ○	○ ○ ○ ○ ○	
Ephemeral	○ ○ ○ ○ ○	○ ○ ○ ○ ○	
Enunciate	○ ○ ○ ○ ○	○ ○ ○ ○ ○	
Cumulative	○ ○ ○ ○ ○	○ ○ ○ ○ ○	
Germane	○ ○ ○ ○ ○	○ ○ ○ ○ ○	
Fascinated	○ ○ ○ ○ ○	○ ○ ○ ○ ○	
Lucid	○ ○ ○ ○ ○	○ ○ ○ ○ ○	
Extraneous	○ ○ ○ ○ ○	○ ○ ○ ○ ○	

Lesson 16

Congratulations on finishing lessons 14-15!

Step back into the thrilling world of 1716, the Golden Age of Piracy, and accompany Captain Blackbeard on a daring quest to capture a Spanish galleon. Your mission: secure the navigational codes to intercept the vessel and plunder its riches. Do you have what it takes to outwit your adversaries and triumph on the vast expanse of the high seas?

Scan the code on your tablet

or copy this link on your browser:

https://natashascripts.com/spanish-galleon/

Password: Blackbeard1716

Here are the words you'll be learning in the next lesson:

Harbinger, Conscientious, Disdain, Implication, Succumb, Retaliate, Endure, Euphemism.

Remember:
- Define Objectives: understand meanings, use in sentences, improve spelling.
- Plan Your Learning Approach: flashcards, write sentences, practice daily, use words in conversations.
- Measure Your Success:
  - Spell all words correctly.
  - Successfully use each word in a sentence.

Word	My Goal	My Strategy	Deadline

Lesson 17

Read the passage to see the target words used in context. Then, complete the questions that follow.

Leadership Styles

In the study of historical leadership, the rise of a leader often serves as a **harbinger** of significant change, signaling shifts in policy and public sentiment. **Conscientious** leaders, those attentive to the ethics and responsibilities of their role, are frequently contrasted with those who govern with **disdain** for dissenting voices. This disdain is not merely an attitude but carries broader **implications** for governance and civil liberties. Leaders who disregard opposing viewpoints may eventually **succumb** to isolation, weakening their governance as they lose touch with the populace.

One common tactic among such leaders is to use **euphemisms** to soften the perception of harsh policies. For instance, describing a forceful suppression of protests as "maintaining public order" can mask the severity of the action. However, history shows that populations will only **endure** so much before they **retaliate**. Retaliation against oppressive leadership can take many forms, from peaceful protests to complete rebellion.

Leaders who endure in memory and respect are often those who have navigated crises without compromising their integrity. They resist the urge to succumb to easy solutions that might compromise their values and instead, face challenges with a **conscientious** approach. Analyzing these patterns helps us understand how leadership styles impact the course of history and the daily lives of people.

1. What can be inferred about the attitude of leaders who are described as having "disdain for dissenting voices" towards public opinion?

A) They are often lauded for their inclusive policies.

B) They tend to isolate themselves from the general populace.

C) They engage frequently in diplomatic negotiations.

D) They prioritize transparency over secrecy.

2. As used in the passage, what does "succumb" most nearly mean?

A) To fight against

B) To yield to

C) To ignore completely

D) To understand deeply

3. According to the passage, what is a possible consequence for leaders who use euphemisms to describe their actions?

A) They may enhance their reputation.

B) They may prevent any form of public dissent.

C) They may mask the severity of their actions.

D) They may gain international support.

4. What function does the comparison between conscientious leaders and those governing with disdain serve in the passage?

A) It illustrates the potential outcomes of different leadership styles.

B) It criticizes modern leadership tactics.

C) It encourages leaders to adopt a more democratic approach.

D) It argues for the necessity of harsh leadership during crises.

5. The author mentions that populations will "only endure so much before they retaliate." What is the primary purpose of this statement?

A) To warn leaders about the limits of public patience.

B) To suggest that all leadership styles eventually fail.

C) To provide a solution for dealing with dissent.

D) To argue for stricter governance to maintain order.

 **Definition and Synonym Match**

Match each word in Column A with its correct definition in Column B and its synonym in Column C. Try to complete the activity on your own first. If you find it absolutely necessary, refer to the Word List and Definitions section for clarification on any words on page 243.

Column A	Column B	Column C
1. Harbinger	**A.** To give in to an overwhelming force or desire.	**i.** Precursor
2. Conscientious	**B.** A mild or indirect word or expression substituted for one considered to be too harsh or blunt.	**ii.** Sneer
3. Disdain	**C.** A sign or warning that something, especially something momentous or calamitous, is likely to happen.	**iii.** Hint
4. Implication	**D.** To continue to exist in the same state; last.	**iv.** Yield
5. Succumb	**E.** Something that is suggested or happens indirectly.	**v.** Last
6. Retaliate	**F.** Scorn, contempt.	**vi.** Meticulous
7. Endure	**G.** To react to an attack by returning the same.	**vii.** Reprisal
8. Euphemism	**H.** Doing one's work diligently and thoroughly.	**viii.** Softening

✎ **Observation: Look closely at each target word below. Circle any letters you find tricky to remember.**

Conscientious

Retaliate   Succumb

Euphemism

Remember:
- **Spot Tricky Letters**
- **Focus Your Efforts**
- **Develop Strategies**

✎ **Break down the words into syllables.**

→   →

Harbinger	har - bin - ger	_____	_____
Conscientious	con - sci - en - tious	_____	_____
Disdain	dis - dain	_____	_____
Implication	im - pli - ca - tion	_____	_____
Succumb	suc - cumb	_____	_____
Retaliate	re - tal - i - ate	_____	_____
Endure	en - dure	_____	_____
Euphemism	eu - phe - mism	_____	_____

✎ **Now write each word in full.**

Harbinger	_____	_____	_____
Conscientious	_____	_____	_____
Disdain	_____	_____	_____
Implication	_____	_____	_____
Succumb	_____	_____	_____
Retaliate	_____	_____	_____
Endure	_____	_____	_____
Euphemism	_____	_____	_____

Select the correct word for each context.

Target Words
Harbinger, Conscientious, Disdain, Implication, Succumb, Retaliate, Endure, Euphemism.

1. Calling the job cuts "streamlining operations" is just a _____ for reducing the workforce to cut costs.

2. The _____ of ignoring the warnings was a series of system failures that could have been avoided.

3. The dark clouds in the sky were a _____ of the upcoming storm.

4. The soldiers had to _____ extreme weather conditions during their training.

5. He viewed their laughter not as friendly jest but as _____, feeling it was directed at his efforts.

6. After the surprise attack on their forces, the generals decided to _____ by launching a counterstrike against the enemy's key military bases.

7. Bella is very _____ about her work; she always double-checks her reports for accuracy.

8. Despite the temptation to give up, she did not _____ to the pressure and continued her climb.

Reflect on your personal experiences and thoughts to answer the following questions using the specified vocabulary words.

1. Think of a time when being conscientious about a task or responsibility significantly affected the outcome. Describe the situation and the role your careful attention to detail played.

----

2. Reflect on a challenge or difficult situation you had to endure in your life. How did you manage to keep going, and what did you learn about yourself from that experience?

----

3. Can you think of a euphemism that people use often in conversations around you? Discuss why you think this euphemism is used instead of the more direct language.

Let's review the words practiced in this lesson and reflect on your confidence in spelling and using the words correctly. Below is a table to guide your self-reflection and self-assessment. Rate your confidence on a scale of 1 to 5, where 1 indicates the least confidence and 5 the most. Then list the words you believe need more practice.

List of Words Practiced	How confident do I feel about spelling each word correctly?	How confident do I feel about using each word in a sentence correctly?	Which words do I need to practice more?
Harbinger	○ ○ ○ ○ ○	○ ○ ○ ○ ○	
Conscientious	○ ○ ○ ○ ○	○ ○ ○ ○ ○	
Disdain	○ ○ ○ ○ ○	○ ○ ○ ○ ○	
Implication	○ ○ ○ ○ ○	○ ○ ○ ○ ○	
Succumb	○ ○ ○ ○ ○	○ ○ ○ ○ ○	
Retaliate	○ ○ ○ ○ ○	○ ○ ○ ○ ○	
Endure	○ ○ ○ ○ ○	○ ○ ○ ○ ○	
Euphemism	○ ○ ○ ○ ○	○ ○ ○ ○ ○	

Here are the words you'll be learning in the next lesson:

Assimilate, Delineate, Hypothesis, Debilitate, Furtive, Haphazard, Disseminate.

Remember:
- Define Objectives: understand meanings, use in sentences, improve spelling.
- Plan Your Learning Approach: flashcards, write sentences, practice daily, use words in conversations.
- Measure Your Success:
  - Spell all words correctly.
  - Successfully use each word in a sentence.

Word	My Goal	My Strategy	Deadline

Lesson 18

✏ **Read the passage to see the target words used in context. Then, complete the questions that follow. Try to complete the activity on your own first. If you find it absolutely necessary, refer to the Word List and Definitions section for clarification on any words on page 243.**

Scientific Report: The Impact of Invasive Species on Local Ecosystems

Introduction

The introduction of non-native species into local ecosystems can often **debilitate** indigenous wildlife, disrupting ecological balance. This report aims to **delineate** the specific impacts observed in the Green Valley region following the inadvertent introduction of the Emerald Beetle.

Methodology

Our research team formulated a **hypothesis** that the rapid spread of the Emerald Beetle would negatively affect the population of native flowering plants. Observations were methodically recorded, avoiding any **haphazard** data collection to ensure reliable results.

Results

Data collected over the past year suggests that native plants have struggled to **assimilate** into their altered environment, leading to a significant decline in their populations. Moreover, a **furtive** predator, the European Pine Marten, previously unobserved in this habitat, has emerged, likely drawn by the weakened state of the native species.

Conclusion

It is imperative that findings be **disseminated** to relevant authorities to prompt remedial action and prevent further ecological damage. Strategies to manage the beetle's population will be crucial to the recovery of Green Valley's ecosystems.

1. In the context of the report, what does "**debilitate**" mean?
A) To strengthen
B) To improve
C) To weaken
D) To stabilize

2. How is "**delineate**" used in the report?
A) To clarify
B) To confuse or mix up
C) To decorate or embellish
D) To remove or erase

3. What does "**hypothesis**" refer to in the methodology section?
A) A proven fact
B) A suggestion without basis
C) A tentative explanation
D) A final conclusion

4. Which option best describes the use of "**furtive**" in the report?
A) Open and noticeable
B) Secretive and sneaky
C) Loud and clear
D) Happy and excited

5. What does "**haphazard**" imply in the context of data collection?
A) Carefully planned
B) Random or disorganized
C) Methodically structured
D) Sequentially ordered

6. What does "**assimilate**" mean as used in the results section?
A) To separate distinctly
B) To resist and fight against
C) To ignore completely
D) To adapt and adjust

7. How is "**disseminate**" used in the conclusion of the report?
A) To collect and compile
B) To diminish or reduce
C) To analyze and interpret
D) To spread or distribute widely

Reread the scientific report and list any words, aside from the target words, that you would like to practice for meaning or spelling.

Spelling   Definition

------------------------   --

------------------------   --

------------------------   --

------------------------   --

------------------------   --

Definition and Synonym Match

Match each word in Column A with its correct definition in Column B and its synonym in Column C.

Column A	Column B	Column C
1. Assimilate	A. To weaken or reduce in strength.	i. Weaken
2. Delineate	B. To distribute or spread information widely.	ii. Stealthy
3. Hypothesis	C. A suggested explanation for a phenomenon made as a starting point for further investigation.	iii. Absorb
4. Debilitate	D. To adapt or become similar to something.	iv. Theory
5. Furtive	E. To outline or describe with precision.	v. Broadcast
6. Haphazard	F. Lacking any obvious principle of organization.	vi. Define
7. Disseminate	G. Stealthy, secretive, or sneaky behavior.	vii. Random

Observation: Look closely at each target word below. Circle any letters you find tricky to remember.

Delineate

Assimilate

Hypothesis   Furtive   Disseminate

Haphazard

 Break down the words into syllables.

→   →

Assimilate	as - sim - i - late	_____	_____
Delineate	de - lin - e - ate	_____	_____
Hypothesis	hy - poth - e - sis	_____	_____
Debilitate	de - bil - i - tate	_____	_____
Furtive	fur - tive	_____	_____
Haphazard	hap - haz - ard	_____	_____
Disseminate	dis - sem - i - nate	_____	_____

 Now write each word in full.

Assimilate	_____	_____	_____
Delineate	_____	_____	_____
Hypothesis	_____	_____	_____
Debilitate	_____	_____	_____
Furtive	_____	_____	_____
Haphazard	_____	_____	_____
Disseminate	_____	_____	_____

Fill each sentence with the appropriate word from the list provided. Use the context of each sentence to determine the correct word.

Target Words
Assimilate, Delineate, Hypothesis, Debilitate, Furtive, Haphazard, Disseminate.

1. The journalist decided to _____ the findings of the corruption investigation across all social media platforms.

2. His _____ glances made it obvious that he was trying to hide something.

3. The scientist's _____ regarding the behavior of gases under pressure was confirmed through rigorous testing.

4. Organizing the files in a _____ manner made it difficult to locate important documents when they were needed.

5. After moving to a new country, it took Tamara a few months to _____ into the local culture.

6. The viral infection _____ him so severely that participating in the marathon became impossible.

7. In the environmental impact study, the researchers needed to _____ the boundaries between the protected wildlife reserve and the proposed development area to assess potential effects accurately.

Complete the following multiple-choice activity by selecting the option that uses each vocabulary word correctly in context.

1. Which of the following best demonstrates the use of the word "**debilitate**"?
A) She was known to debilitate her time between studies and sports efficiently.
B) The chef's ability to debilitate flavors in the dish was praised by everyone.
C) The debate team's argument was so strong that it debilitated their opponents' confidence.
D) The windows were debilitated to prevent any drafts during the winter.

2. Which sentence uses "**delineate**" correctly?
A) He promised to delineate his brother at the family reunion.
B) The architect used her blueprint to delineate the areas that would need more support.
C) The committee worked hard to delineate the funds for the next fiscal year.
D) She planned to delineate her hair before attending the formal event.

3. Choose the sentence where "**furtive**" is used appropriately.
A) The furtive meal was enjoyed by all the guests at the party.
B) She made a furtive decision to move to a new city.
C) The gardener used a furtive to trim the bushes in the backyard.
D) His furtive glances at the clock made it clear he was eager to leave.

4. Select the option that correctly uses "**disseminate**."
A) They planned to disseminate the old furniture over the weekend.
B) The journalist sought to disseminate the information through an online blog.
C) The team captain will disseminate the position of goalkeeper this season.
D) She was advised to disseminate her investments among various options.

5. Which of the following best describes the use of the word "**assimilate**"?

A) The family tried to assimilate their old furniture into the modern decor of their new home.

B) He assimilated his schedule to include more time for exercise.

C) After moving to France, she quickly assimilated into the local culture.

D) The company's CEO will assimilate the new policies by the end of the quarter.

6. Which sentence uses "**hypothesis**" correctly?

A) After reviewing the data, he formed a hypothesis that increased sunlight would boost plant growth.

B) The scientist won an award for proving his hypothesis about water pollution.

C) Her hypothesis about the outcome of the election was incorrect.

D) He wrote a hypothesis in his diary every night.

7. Choose the sentence where "**haphazard**" is used appropriately.

A) They followed a haphazard which led them directly to the treasure.

B) She delivered a haphazard speech that captivated the audience.

C) The chef's haphazard approach to baking the cake surprisingly worked.

D) The documents were organized in a haphazard manner, making it difficult to find anything.

Let's review the words practiced in this lesson and reflect on your confidence in spelling and using the words correctly. Below is a table to guide your self-reflection and self-assessment. Rate your confidence on a scale of 1 to 5, where 1 indicates the least confidence and 5 the most. Then list the words you believe need more practice.

List of Words Practiced	How confident do I feel about spelling each word correctly?	How confident do I feel about using each word in a sentence correctly?	Which words do I need to practice more?
Assimilate	○ ○ ○ ○ ○	○ ○ ○ ○ ○	
Delineate	○ ○ ○ ○ ○	○ ○ ○ ○ ○	
Hypothesis	○ ○ ○ ○ ○	○ ○ ○ ○ ○	
Debilitate	○ ○ ○ ○ ○	○ ○ ○ ○ ○	
Furtive	○ ○ ○ ○ ○	○ ○ ○ ○ ○	
Haphazard	○ ○ ○ ○ ○	○ ○ ○ ○ ○	
Disseminate	○ ○ ○ ○ ○	○ ○ ○ ○ ○	

Setting Goals for the Upcoming Lesson

Here are the words you'll be learning in the next lesson:

Erratic, Concur, Denounce, Deter, Genesis, Fallacy, Fathom, Idiosyncrasy.

Remember:
- Define Objectives: understand meanings, use in sentences, improve spelling.
- Plan Your Learning Approach: flashcards, write sentences, practice daily, use words in conversations.
- Measure Your Success:
  - Spell all words correctly.
  - Successfully use each word in a sentence.

Word	My Goal	My Strategy	Deadline

Lesson 19

In this activity, you'll explore the use of a specific word across different contexts and expressions. You'll first identify its meaning through context, then apply it in a sentence, and finally, practice its spelling. Try to complete the activity on your own first. If you find it absolutely necessary, refer to the Word List and Definitions section for clarification on any words. This exercise aims to deepen your understanding of the word's usage and enhance your writing skills.

Erratic

1. Jason's **erratic** driving made it difficult for his friends to relax in the car; one minute they were cruising smoothly, and the next, they were swerving sharply.

2. The stock market displayed **erratic** behavior last week, with prices soaring and plummeting without any clear reason, leaving investors puzzled and anxious.

3. The teacher noticed that Karen's attendance had become **erratic** over the semester, varying wildly from week to week with no discernible pattern or explanation.

1. What does the word "erratic" mean as used in the sentences above?

A) Rapid and predictable

B) Regular and stable

C) Irregular and unpredictable

D) Slow and cautious

Complete the sentence starters below that contain the target word. Ensure your completion accurately reflects its meaning in context.

2. The cat's behavior became erratic when _____

_____.

3. Due to his erratic sleep schedule, he _____

_____.

4. The car's erratic movements alarmed the passengers because _____

_____.

Concur

1. After a long debate, the committee members finally began to **concur** with the chairman's proposal, nodding in agreement as they saw the benefits it offered.
2. Although initially skeptical, Jessica came to **concur** with her partner's strategy on the project after seeing the positive results of a similar approach.
3. During the literature review, most of the book club members seemed to **concur** with the interpretation that the protagonist's actions were motivated by loyalty rather than greed.

5. What does the word "concur" mean as used in the sentences above?

A) To agree or have the same opinion
B) To disagree strongly
C) To have a different opinion
D) To argue about a topic

Complete the sentence starters below that contain the target word. Ensure your completion accurately reflects its meaning in context.

6. After reviewing all the evidence presented in the debate, I finally had to concur that

_____

_____.

7. Although it was not my initial thought, I concur with the decision to _____

_____ because

_____.

8. While I rarely concur with her opinions on movies, this time I agree that _____

_____

_____.

Denounce

1. During the town hall meeting, several community leaders stood up to **denounce** the new policy, arguing that it would harm local businesses.

2. The environmental group decided to **denounce** the corporation publicly for its role in the river pollution, demanding immediate action to remedy the situation.

3. In her speech, the candidate did not hesitate to **denounce** the unfair practices her opponent had used during the campaign, calling for a return to honest and transparent elections.

9. What does the word "denounce" mean as used in the sentences above?

A) To publicly declare support for an issue

B) To quietly disagree without making it public

C) To publicly express strong disapproval

D) To acknowledge something reluctantly

Complete the sentence starters below that contain the target word. Ensure your completion accurately reflects its meaning in context.

10. Despite feeling nervous, I stood up in class to denounce _____

_____.

11. In our society, we need to denounce behaviors like _____

_____.

12. The whistleblower bravely denounced _____

_____.

Deter

1. The heavy rain did not **deter** the fans from lining up hours before the concert, equipped with umbrellas and raincoats.

2. High prices at the cafeteria seemed to **deter** students from buying their lunch at school, leading many to bring meals from home instead.

3. The threat of harsh penalties is often used to **deter** people from breaking the law, aiming to maintain order and safety in the community.

13. What does the word "deter" mean as used in the sentences above?

A) To encourage participation in an activity

B) To hasten an action or decision

C) To assist someone in achieving a goal

D) To prevent or discourage someone from doing something

Complete the sentence starters below that contain the target word. Ensure your completion accurately reflects its meaning in context.

14. Implementing stricter consequences for littering can help deter _____

_____.

15. Adding more lighting in dark alleys is a method to deter _____

_____.

16. Installing security cameras around the school can deter _____

_____.

Genesis

1. The **genesis** of the internet revolutionized communication worldwide, beginning as a simple network among academic institutions.
2. The documentary traced the **genesis** of jazz music in America, highlighting its roots in the African American communities of the South.
3. Her interest in environmental science had its **genesis** during a high school project on renewable energy, sparking a lifelong passion and career.

17. What does the word "genesis" mean as used in the sentences above?

A) The origin or beginning of something
B) The conclusion or end of an event
C) A change or transformation
D) A continuation of a process

Complete the sentence starters below that contain the target word. Ensure your completion accurately reflects its meaning in context.

18. The genesis of my interest in science began when _____

_____.

19. Exploring the genesis of ancient civilizations helps us understand _____

_____.

20. The genesis of the conflict can be traced back to _____

_____.

Fallacy

1. The teacher explained that it was a **fallacy** to believe that heavier objects fall faster than lighter ones, using experiments to demonstrate the truth.

2. He pointed out the **fallacy** in the argument that colder weather disproves global warming, clarifying how weather and climate are distinctly different.

3. During the debate, she quickly exposed the **fallacy** of her opponent's claim that technology always leads to decreased physical activity, citing numerous tech-driven fitness innovations.

21. What does the word "fallacy" mean as used in the sentences above?

A) A widely accepted truth

B) A method of logical reasoning

C) An unintentional mistake

D) A mistaken belief or error in reasoning

Complete the sentence starters below that contain the target word. Ensure your completion accurately reflects its meaning in context.

22. The argument presented by the politician was based on a fallacy because _____

_____.

23. The belief that the earth is flat is a fallacy because _____

_____.

24. A historical fallacy in US history is the idea of "Manifest Destiny" because _____

_____

_____.

Fathom

1. She struggled to **fathom** the depth of her friend's grief after the loss, finding it hard to offer the right comfort.

2. The ancient astronomers could barely **fathom** the vastness of the universe, marveling at the night sky with basic telescopes.

3. After studying the diagrams and equations, Sarah still couldn't **fathom** the principles behind quantum mechanics, finding the concepts too abstract and complex.

25. What does the word "fathom" mean as used in the sentences above?

A) To reject or deny something strongly

B) To measure the depth of water

C) To understand something deeply and fully

D) To explore or investigate

Complete the sentence starters below that contain the target word. Ensure your completion accurately reflects its meaning in context.

26. The depth of the ocean was so immense that I couldn't fathom _____

_____.

27. As I read about historical events, I found it hard to fathom _____

_____.

28. The idea of time travel is something I can't fathom because _____

_____.

Idiosyncrasy

1. His **idiosyncrasy** of organizing books by color instead of author or genre made his library a visually striking but somewhat impractical space.

2. The new teacher's **idiosyncrasy** of starting every class with a motivational quote quickly endeared her to the students.

3. Everyone knew about the mayor's **idiosyncrasy**; he would never attend a meeting without his lucky pen, claiming it helped him think better.

29. What does the word "idiosyncrasy" mean as used in the sentences above?

A) A habitual gesture or way of speaking shared by a large group

B) An unusual feature or habit unique to an individual

C) A common tradition or practice in a community

D) A typical characteristic seen in most people

Complete the sentence starters below that contain the target word. Ensure your completion accurately reflects its meaning in context.

30. One idiosyncrasy of mine is _____

_____.

31. Understanding the cultural idiosyncrasies of different countries can _____

_____.

32. Despite his idiosyncrasies, he was respected for his _____

_____.

🖉 **Observation: Look closely at each target word below. Circle any letters you find tricky to remember.**

Erratic   Deter   Concur

Denounce   Genesis

Idiosyncrasy

Fathom

Fallacy

🖉 **Break down the words into syllables.**

→ → →

Erratic	er - rat - ic	_____	_____
Concur	con - cur	_____	_____
Denounce	de - nounce	_____	_____
Deter	de - ter	_____	_____
Genesis	gen - e - sis	_____	_____
Fallacy	fal - la - cy	_____	_____
Fathom	fath - om	_____	_____
Idiosyncrasy	id - i - o - syn - cra - sy	_____	_____

✏️ **Now write each word in full.**

Erratic _____ _____ _____

Concur _____ _____ _____

Denounce _____ _____ _____

Deter _____ _____ _____

Genesis _____ _____ _____

Fallacy _____ _____ _____

Fathom _____ _____ _____

Idiosyncrasy _____ _____ _____

Let's review the words practiced in this lesson and reflect on your confidence in spelling and using the words correctly. Below is a table to guide your self-reflection and self-assessment. Rate your confidence on a scale of 1 to 5, where 1 indicates the least confidence and 5 the most. Then list the words you believe need more practice.

List of Words Practiced	How confident do I feel about spelling each word correctly?	How confident do I feel about using each word in a sentence correctly?	Which words do I need to practice more?
Erratic	○ ○ ○ ○ ○	○ ○ ○ ○ ○	
Concur	○ ○ ○ ○ ○	○ ○ ○ ○ ○	
Denounce	○ ○ ○ ○ ○	○ ○ ○ ○ ○	
Deter	○ ○ ○ ○ ○	○ ○ ○ ○ ○	
Genesis	○ ○ ○ ○ ○	○ ○ ○ ○ ○	
Fallacy	○ ○ ○ ○ ○	○ ○ ○ ○ ○	
Fathom	○ ○ ○ ○ ○	○ ○ ○ ○ ○	
Idiosyncrasy	○ ○ ○ ○ ○	○ ○ ○ ○ ○	

Here are the words you'll be learning in the next lesson:

Diffuse, Diligence, Extrapolate, Fervent, Viable, Scrutiny, Redundant, Proponent.

Remember:
- Define Objectives: understand meanings, use in sentences, improve spelling.
- Plan Your Learning Approach: flashcards, write sentences, practice daily, use words in conversations.
- Measure Your Success:
  - Spell all words correctly.
  - Successfully use each word in a sentence.

Word	My Goal	My Strategy	Deadline

Lesson 20

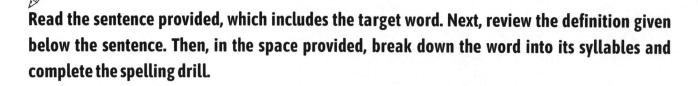

Read the sentence provided, which includes the target word. Next, review the definition given below the sentence. Then, in the space provided, break down the word into its syllables and complete the spelling drill.

Diffuse, Diligence, Extrapolate, Fervent, Viable, Scrutiny, Redundant, Proponent.

1. 1. The morning sun **diffused** a warm glow through the curtains, lighting up the classroom softly.

Definition of "Diffuse" : To spread something widely or throughout an area, especially information, ideas, or particles.

dif - fuse ⟶ _____ _____ _____

diffuse ⟶ _____ _____ _____

2. Her **diligence** in studying for the exams paid off when she scored the highest in her class.

Definition of "Diligence": Careful and persistent work or effort; paying detailed attention to a task.

dil - i - gence ⟶ _____ _____ _____

diligence ⟶ _____ _____ _____

3. Based on the first half of the game's scoring trends, we can **extrapolate** that the final score might be close.

Definition of "Extrapolate" : To use known information to make guesses or predictions about something unknown.

ex - trap - o - late → _____ _____ _____

extrapolate → _____ _____ _____

4. He had a **fervent** belief in justice, which led him to volunteer at the community legal aid.

Definition of "Fervent": Having or showing very strong and sincere feelings about something, especially beliefs or interests.

fer - vent → _____ _____ _____

fervent → _____ _____ _____

5. Solar energy is becoming a more **viable** option as technology improves and costs decrease.

Definition of "Viable" : Capable of working successfully; feasible or practical.

vi - a - ble ⟶ _____ _____ _____

viable ⟶ _____ _____ _____

6. The new policy was under heavy **scrutiny** by the board to ensure it addressed all the previous issues.

Definition of "Scrutiny": Close and careful examination or observation, often to find details or flaws.

scr - ti - ny ⟶ _____ _____ _____

scrutiny ⟶ _____ _____ _____

7. After revising my argumentative essay, I realized that some points were **redundant** and removed them to make my writing clearer.

Definition of "Redundant": Unnecessary because it is more than what is needed.

re - dun - dant ⟶ _____ _____ _____

redundant ⟶ _____ _____ _____

8. Our ELA teacher is a strong **proponent** of digital learning, advocating for more online activities to be available to students.

Definition of "Proponent": A person who advocates for or supports a particular idea, cause, or proposal.

pro - po - nent ⟶ _____ _____ _____

proponent ⟶ _____ _____ _____

Read the passage to see the target words used in context. Then, complete the questions that follow.

The Transformative Impact of Emerging Technologies on Society

Emerging technologies represent the forefront of innovation and potential societal transformation. Defined broadly, these technologies include developments like artificial intelligence, blockchain, and biotechnology, which are not only advancing rapidly but are also becoming increasingly **viable** for widespread application. These technologies promise to revolutionize industries, improve daily living, and address complex societal challenges.

The benefits of emerging technologies are extensive and varied. In healthcare, for instance, AI-driven diagnostics are enhancing the accuracy and speed of patient care, significantly improving outcomes. **Proponents** of these technologies are **fervent** in their advocacy, citing potential breakthroughs in treatment methods and patient management. They foresee a future where technology and medicine intertwine to eradicate diseases.

However, these technologies are not without their challenges. The introduction of autonomous vehicles and AI in various sectors has sparked intense **scrutiny** over safety, ethics, and employment impacts. It requires great **diligence** from regulators and developers to address these concerns effectively. Continuous monitoring and evaluation are crucial to ensure that the deployment of these technologies does not inadvertently create new problems.

Information about these emerging technologies **diffuses** rapidly across digital and traditional media, reaching a global audience in real-time. However, the **redundancy** of information— repetitive data that confirms or supports existing data—plays a critical role in reinforcing the reliability of these technological innovations. In technology systems, **redundant** components are crucial for ensuring system reliability, particularly in scenarios where a single point of failure could lead to catastrophic outcomes.

Looking ahead, one can **extrapolate** that the integration of smart technologies into everyday life will only increase, potentially leading to smart cities and homes where technology manages everything from energy use to security. However, predicting these trends requires careful consideration of current trajectories and potential technological advancements. Such predictions help stakeholders prepare for and shape future developments effectively.

Emerging technologies undeniably hold the potential to significantly impact all aspects of society. As we stand on the brink of these vast changes, it is imperative to balance innovation with caution. We must question not just what technology can do, but what it should do. As members of a global society, it is our responsibility to engage with and shape these technologies, ensuring they serve to enhance, rather than diminish, the quality of human life.

1. How is the word "viable" used in the passage?

A) To describe the uncertain potential of emerging technologies.

B) To describe the slow progress of technology development.

C) To describe technologies that are practical and capable of working successfully.

D) To describe technologies that are outdated and no longer useful.

2. What does "proponent" refer to in the context of the passage?

A) A person who opposes emerging technologies.

B) A person who supports or advocates for emerging technologies.

C) A technology that is no longer in use.

D) A method of developing technology.

3. In the passage, "fervent" is used to describe:

A) The intense passion of those advocating for emerging technologies.

B) The cautious approach of regulators.

C) The slow adoption of new technologies.

D) The potential dangers of technology.

4. What does "scrutiny" imply in the passage?

A) Ignorance toward potential risks.

B) A brief examination of emerging technologies.

C) Careful, critical examination.

D) Quick approval of technological innovations.

5. The word "diffuses" in the passage means:

A) Consolidates information in a single source.

B) Ignored widely by the public.

C) Collects information from global sources.

D) Spreads information widely.

6. How is "redundant" used in the context of the passage?

A) As describing unnecessary or repetitive components.

B) As describing outdated technology.

C) As describing components essential for modern communication.

D) As describing components that decrease system reliability.

7. To "extrapolate" in the passage means to:

A) Disregard all current data about technologies.

B) Make decisions based on incomplete data.

C) Extend current trends to predict future developments.

D) Reduce the impact of technology on society.

8. What does "diligence" mean as used in the passage?

A) Negligence by regulators and developers.

B) The speed at which technology is adopted.

C) Careful and persistent work or effort by those overseeing technology implementation.

D) Lack of interest in following up on technology development.

1. Reflect on your understanding of the words practiced in this lesson. Can you define each word accurately?

Diffuse: _____

Diligence: _____

Extrapolate: _____

Fervent: _____

Viable: _____

Scrutiny: _____

Redundant: _____

Proponent: _____

Example: Think about something in your life that you find redundant but that your parents loved when they were young. What is it, and why do you think it's no longer necessary or efficient today?

One thing I find redundant that my parents loved when they were young is burning CDs for music. My parents used to spend hours making mix CDs and labeling them. Today, with streaming services like Spotify and Apple Music, making CDs seems unnecessary because you can have millions of songs instantly without needing physical storage. I think CDs are no longer efficient because digital music is more accessible and environmentally friendly, as it reduces waste.

2. Write about a time when your diligence in a project or hobby paid off. Describe the effort you put in, any obstacles you faced, and the outcome of your persistence. How did this experience teach you the value of hard work?

_____

_____

_____

_____

_____

_____

_____

3. Reflect on something that you are fervent about, whether it's a cause, a hobby, or a subject in school. Describe how you discovered this passion and what actions you take to engage with it. How has your fervor influenced others around you?

----

4. Think of a time when you or something you did was under intense scrutiny. How did you feel and respond to this situation? What did you learn about yourself from this experience, and how did it affect your future actions or decisions?

Let's review the words practiced in this lesson and reflect on your confidence in spelling and using the words correctly. Below is a table to guide your self-reflection and self-assessment. Rate your confidence on a scale of 1 to 5, where 1 indicates the least confidence and 5 the most. Then list the words you believe need more practice.

List of Words Practiced	How confident do I feel about spelling each word correctly?	How confident do I feel about using each word in a sentence correctly?	Which words do I need to practice more?
Diffuse	○ ○ ○ ○ ○	○ ○ ○ ○ ○	
Diligence	○ ○ ○ ○ ○	○ ○ ○ ○ ○	
Extrapolate	○ ○ ○ ○ ○	○ ○ ○ ○ ○	
Fervent	○ ○ ○ ○ ○	○ ○ ○ ○ ○	
Viable	○ ○ ○ ○ ○	○ ○ ○ ○ ○	
Scrutiny	○ ○ ○ ○ ○	○ ○ ○ ○ ○	
Redundant	○ ○ ○ ○ ○	○ ○ ○ ○ ○	
Proponent	○ ○ ○ ○ ○	○ ○ ○ ○ ○	

To solidify your understanding and mastery of the vocabulary you've encountered, I encourage you to revisit the Word List with Definitions section on page 243. This review will help reinforce the great work you've done throughout our lessons.

Instructions for Review:

1. **Break It Down:** Tackle about 20 words daily.
2. **Test Yourself:** Write each word's definition from memory, then check your accuracy.
3. **Practice Makes Perfect:** Use each word in a sentence to enhance your understanding.
4. **Pair Up:** Quiz each other with a friend to make reviewing fun and interactive.
5. **Stay Consistent:** Dedicate a regular time each day to focus on your review.

This focused approach will boost your vocabulary retention and confidence. Keep challenging yourself and exploring new words!

Congratulations!

Dear Student,

Well done on completing this workbook! You have worked diligently through 20 intensive lessons. Your commitment to expanding your spelling and word usage is truly commendable.

As you celebrate this achievement, remember that learning is a continuous process. I invite you now to take the online tests associated with this workbook. These tests will give you a score that reflects your understanding of the vocabulary you've learned. Don't worry if you encounter any challenges; they are opportunities for further learning. If you find any difficulties or incorrect answers, I encourage you to revisit the lessons and review the definitions and word usage explanations. This approach will deepen your understanding and reinforce your learning.

Keep this workbook as a reference book. It will serve as a valuable resource as you continue to encounter new reading materials and writing tasks in the future.

Congratulations once again on your hard work and dedication. Keep striving for excellence in all that you do!

Best wishes,

Natasha Attard Ph.D

Final Test

You are encouraged to take the final online test. This test is designed to evaluate your understanding of the academic vocabulary we've covered, which includes the most commonly used words in literature and specific domain vocabulary relevant to your studies.

Test Details:
- Number of Questions: 25
- Points per Question: 4
- Total Possible Points: 100

Once you submit your answers, you will receive your score immediately. This will include details on which questions you answered correctly and which ones you did not, allowing you to see where your strengths lie and areas where you may need further review.

Take this opportunity to demonstrate your knowledge and see how much you've learned. Good luck!

https://natashascripts.com/final-test

Password: Finaltest9-10

Answer Key

Lesson 1 : The Discovery of Atlantis

1. How can you determine if this document is accurate and reliable?
By cross-referencing information with other sources, assessing the credibility of the author, examining the evidence provided, and identifying potential biases or conflicts of interest.

2. Does this document contain a chronological order of events and if so, what are they?
Yes, the document outlines the events of the expedition in chronological order, from the initial discovery to the subsequent analysis of artifacts.

3.What historical context does this document refer to?
The document references the legend of Atlantis as described by Plato and situates the discovery within the broader context of archaeological exploration and scientific inquiry.

4. In what context does Professor Westfield encourage rigor?
Professor Westfield encourages rigor in the study of Atlantis, urging scholars to approach the evidence with an open mind and conduct further study and excavation.

5. What tone does this document have? Is it formal or informal? How accessible is this document to people who are not familiar with the subject?
The document has a formal tone appropriate for scholarly discourse. It is accessible to readers unfamiliar with the subject, as it provides clear explanations and context for the significance of the discovery of Atlantis.

Lesson 2
Word Scramble

CRITERIA
ASSESS
VULNERABLE
FORTIFY
DECIPHER
CONCEAL
AMBIGUOUS
Mystery Word:
termite

The Great American Pizza Quest

rigorously   reliable   accessible

rigorous   reliable   accessibility

context

Define in context

1. To "assess" a project means to evaluate or judge how well the project was done. In this case, the teacher is looking at each student's project to see how original it is and how much effort was put into it. This helps the teacher decide how successful each student was in completing the project according to the criteria given.

2. In the context of a competition, "criteria" are the standards or rules that the judges use to evaluate and score the entries. For this competition, the criteria include creativity, technique, and presentation. This means that the judges will look at how creative each entry is, how well the techniques are applied, and how effectively the work is presented to determine the winners.

3. Something is described as "vulnerable" when it is not protected well and is easily hurt or damaged. In this sentence, the smartphone is called vulnerable because, without its protective case, it can easily get scratches or other kinds of damage from being dropped or bumped.

4. To "fortify" something means to make it stronger or more secure. In this sentence, the city is fortifying its flood defenses, which means it is strengthening or enhancing the structures or systems that protect it from flooding. This is being done in response to rising water levels, to help prevent water damage and keep the city safe.

5. To "decipher" when dealing with ancient texts means to figure out or interpret the meaning of writings that are difficult to understand because of age, wear, or the use of a now unfamiliar language or script. Archaeologists often need to decipher these texts to uncover the historical significance and information they contain, which can help us learn more about the past and the people who lived then.

6. To "conceal" something means to hide it so that it cannot be seen or found easily. In this sentence, the spy needs to conceal the documents carefully, which means he must hide them in such a way that no one can detect or discover them, ensuring they remain secret and secure.

7. Directions are described as "ambiguous" when they are not clear or specific, and can be understood in more than one way. Ambiguous directions can be problematic because they can lead to confusion and uncertainty, as they don't provide clear guidance on what should be done. In the case of the hikers, the ambiguous directions made them unsure of which path to take, which could potentially lead to them getting lost or taking a longer route.

8. In the context of scientific research, to "formulate" means to create or develop a statement or theory that can be tested through experiments. In this sentence, the scientist took weeks to formulate a hypothesis, meaning they spent time developing a precise and testable idea based on their research goals.

9. The word "desolate" describes a scene that appears empty, abandoned, and bleak. In the context of the beach after the storm, it suggests a lonely and forlorn landscape with debris scattered around and no people visible.

10. When someone is "exhausted," they feel extremely tired, worn out, and have very little energy left, often to the point where they find it difficult to continue with physical activities or even simple tasks.

11. "Empathy" is important in a counseling session because it helps the counselor understand and share the feelings of the student. This emotional connection makes the student feel supported and valued.

12. The purpose of taking medicine to "alleviate" symptoms is to reduce their severity and provide relief, making the patient feel more comfortable and helping them recover more quickly.

Lesson 4:
Rewriting Sentences

1a. Bipedal animals, including birds and humans, have evolved specialized skeletal structures and muscular systems to support their locomotion.
1b. Specialized skeletal structures and muscular systems have evolved to support the locomotion of bipedal animals like birds and humans.
2a. The verdant meadow stretched out before us, vibrant with color and life.
2b. Vibrant with color and life, the verdant meadow stretched out before us.
3. The adventurer roamed through the dense jungle, exploring its mysteries.
4a. Paleontologists study fossils to learn about prehistoric life.
4b. To learn about prehistoric life, paleontologists study fossils.
5a. The formidable mountain loomed over the landscape, impressing all who beheld its majesty.
5b. Impressing all who beheld its majesty, the formidable mountain loomed over the landscape.
6a. The extinction of the Dodo, a flightless bird native to Mauritius, was caused by human activities and habitat destruction.
6b. The Dodo, a flightless bird native to Mauritius, has become extinct due to human activities and habitat destruction.
6c. Due to human activities and habitat destruction, the Dodo, a flightless bird native to Mauritius, has gone extinct.

Hidden Synonyms
Remains, Intimidating, Critical, Lush

7a. Scientists examine the anatomy of living organisms to understand their biology.
7b. To understand their biology, scientists study the anatomy of living organisms.
8a. Effective communication is crucial for building strong relationships and fostering teamwork.
8b. Building strong relationships and fostering teamwork is crucially dependent on effective communication.

Word Search

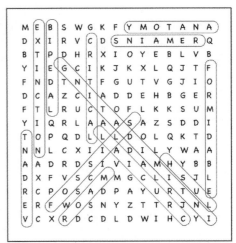

ANATOMY	BIPEDAL	CRITICAL
CRUCIAL	EXTINCTION	FORMIDABLE
FOSSILS	INTIMIDATING	LUSH
REMAINS	ROAM	VERDANT

Lesson 5:
Deciphering Image Meaning

hieroglyphics

devastate/devastating

perpetrate

archaeologists

cuneiform

resilience

pivotal, e.g. a pivotal moment in life

collapse

Lesson 7: Proofreading

1 1. exposition, 2. depict, 3. dynamics, 4. excerpt, 5. diary, 6. fascinating, 7. witness.

2 1. mediate, 2. negotiation, 3. compromise, 4. sunbathing, 5. incoherent, 6. exploit.

3 1. competition, 2. compelling, 3. bias, 4. excerpts, 5. correlation, 6. exploitation, 7. mediate.

Lesson 8: Fill-in-the-Blank

1. Eminent	1. Falter
2. Prevalent	2. Intercede
3. Audacious	3. Censure
4. Eminent	4. Falter
5. Affiliation	5. Cynic
6. Prevalent	6. Constrained
7. Audacious	7. Intercede
8. Affiliation	8. Censure
	9. Cynic
	10. Constrained

Lesson 8: Synonyms Word Search

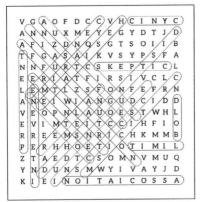

```
V G A O F D C C V H C I N Y C
A N N U X M E Y E G Y D T J D
A F I Z D N Q S G T S O I B
T F G A S A I K V S Y P S F A
N N F U R T C S K E P T I C L
E E R I A T F I R S I V C L C
L N E M T L Z S F O N F E F R N
A N E I W I A N G U D C I D D
V E O P N L A U O E S T W H L
E V I M T E I T C C I H F I O
R R E E M S N R I C H K M M B
P E R H H O E T I O T I M I L
Z T A E D T C S O M V M U Q
Y N D U N S M W Y I V A Y J D
K I E I N O I T A I C O S S A
```

AFFILIATION	ASSOCIATION	AUDACIOUS
BOLD	CENSURE	COMMON
CONSTRAIN	CRITICISM	CYNIC
DISTINGUISHED	EMINENT	FALTER
HESITATE	INTERCEDE	INTERVENE
LIMIT	PREVALENT	SKEPTIC

Synonyms

Prevalent - common	Falter - hesitate
Affiliation - association	Cynic - skeptic
Eminent - distinguished	
Audacious - bold	
Censure - criticism	
Constrain - limit	
Intercede - intervene	

Lesson 9: Fill-in-the-blank

1. Deductive	5. Hackneyed
2. Hackneyed	6. Deductive
3. Aesthetic	7. Aesthetic
4. Exhaustive	8. Exhaustive

Lesson 9: Image Captioning

Strong Disapproval

Answer 1: The The activists deplore the ongoing deforestation and environmental degradation.

Answer 2: The activists condemn the reckless actions of industries contributing to the planet's harm.

Structural Beauty

The ancient Egyptians valued aesthetic beauty in structures, which is evidenced by the majestic pyramids and temples they constructed.

Answer may vary

Reasoning to a Conclusion

The archaeologist employs deductive reasoning to piece together the history of ancient civilizations.

Answer may vary

Thorough Research

He carried out exhaustive research to reach his conclusions.

Answer may vary

Lesson 10: Multiple Choice

1. B
2. C
3. D
4. A
5. C

Fill-in-the-Blank

1. Exhilarating
2. Guile
3. Candid
4. Reconcile
5. Gregarious

Crossword Puzzle

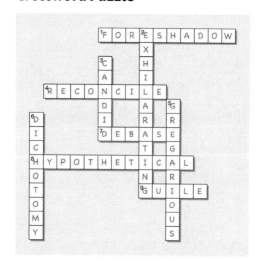

Lesson 11

Fill-in-the-Blank

1. Coerce
2. Foreseeable
3. Declamation
4. Judicious
5. Loquacious
6. Escalate

Synonyms

Predictable - Foreseeable

Force - Coerce

Speech - Declamation

Wise - Judicious

Intensify - Escalate

Waste - Squander

Chatty - Loquacious

Size - Magnitude

Ambiguous - Equivocal

Word Match

1. Coerce/Coerces
2. Squander/Squanders
3. Escalate/Escalation
4. Foresee/Foreseeable
5. Declamation
6. Equivocal
7. Judicious
8. Loquacious
9. Magnitude

Lesson 12

1. tirade
2. B
3. C - vexation
4. Madison decides not to use a pseudonym to answer the angry comments because she is committed to transparency and facing criticism head-on, despite the backlash.
5. She demonstrates resilience, determination, transparency and commitment to her beliefs.
6. A
7. Engaging in online debates about controversial topics can be challenging because you face a lot of criticism and negativity, like Madison did. It's hard not to take it personally, and sometimes it feels like you're not making a difference. But there are also benefits. You get to share your opinions and learn from others, and if you handle it well, you can change people's minds or at least make them think differently. It's important to stay calm and respectful, even when people disagree with you.
8. I think Emily made the right choice by addressing the criticism directly. Even though it was hard, it showed that she was confident in her beliefs and willing to stand up for them. Avoiding the criticism might have made things worse in the long run because people would still be talking about her blog post and spreading negativity. By responding, she had a chance to explain her ideas and maybe change some minds. It also showed that she was brave and not afraid to face challenges head-on.

ANSWERS MAY VARY

Lesson 12 : Fill-in-the-Blank

1. Ubiquity
2. Constructive
3. Dissent
4. Contrive

5. Ubiquity
6. Contrive
7. Dissent
8. Constructive

Image Interpretation

Tirade

Advocating

Ubiquity

Palpable

Dissent

Vexation

Constructive

Pseudonym

Lesson 14: Application and Writing Integration

1. B

2. To ensure no confusion, the teacher's assignment instructions were explicit.

3. During the review, his feedback on my presentation was explicit.

4. To prevent any disputes, the terms and conditions of the contract were explicit.

5. C

6. The community activists were infuriated by the unjust ruling of the judge.

7. His project partner was infuriated by his continual procrastination.

8. She was infuriated by the mocking tone in his voice.

9. C

10. The peaceful setting of the garden is conducive to meditation and reflection.

11. The coach's supportive approach is conducive to a positive environment for team growth.

12. Having a dedicated workspace at home is conducive to maintaining productivity during remote work.

13. B

14. Subverting

15. Undermining

16. Disrupting

17. B

18. The board of directors **strayed** from the scheduled agenda, causing the meeting to extend by two hours.

19. During his presentation he **veered** off the topic, which caused confusion among the audience.

20. She had to **diverge** from her usual routine to accommodate the new project.

Fill-in-the-Blank

1. Lyrical
2. Exonerate
3. Elation
4. Lyrical
5. Profound
6. Elation
7. Exonerated
8. Profound

Extended Writing Practice: Model Answers

1. To make my favorite spaghetti carbonara, start by boiling water in a large pot. Add a pinch of salt. Once boiling, add spaghetti and cook for 8 minutes. In a separate pan, cook chopped bacon until crispy. Beat two eggs with a half cup of grated Parmesan cheese. Then drain the pasta and return it to the pot. Quickly stir in the egg and cheese mixture, making sure the eggs do not scramble. Add the crispy bacon, mix everything thoroughly, and serve immediately with extra cheese.

2. My younger brother infuriates me by borrowing my things without asking and then misplacing them. I often find myself scrambling to locate my missing headphones or books, like the time I missed the school bus because I was searching everywhere. His carelessness not only drives me up the wall but also forces me to keep my things locked up.

3. Karina, driven by her eagerness to win the science fair, decided to sabotage her main competitor's project—a solar-powered coffee maker. She sneaked into the main hall where the projects were displayed and removed a small chip from the mini-solar panel. As she anticipated, the coffee maker malfunctioned during the judges' review. However, Karina's actions were captured on the school's security cameras, and as a result, she was disqualified from the competition.

4. Last summer, while hiking in the Rockies, I planned to follow the marked trails but deviated to explore a less-traveled path I stumbled upon. This deviation led to discovering a secluded waterfall. The sight was breathtaking, and the serenity of the location was unmatched. This unexpected detour was a highlight of my trip, demonstrating that often the most memorable adventures are those that aren't planned.

5. Jake, a junior, was accused of using AI to write his history paper. Facing potential disciplinary action, he presented the edit history from Google Docs during a meeting with the school administration. The time-stamped evidence clearly documented his personal input and revisions over time. He felt relieved to be able to exonerate himself with the evidence he provided.

Extended Writing Practice: Model Answers

6. The meadow was bathed in the golden light of the setting sun, casting long shadows and illuminating the wildflowers that swayed gently in the breeze. The air was filled with the sweet fragrance of honeysuckle, and the distant sound of a river provided a soothing background melody. This scene was like a lyrical poem composed by nature itself, evoking feelings of peace and a deep connection with the natural world around me.

7. Recently, I had a profound realization about the impact of kindness. While volunteering at a local shelter, I noticed how a simple act of kindness, like a warm meal and a few comforting words, significantly uplifted the spirits of those going through tough times. This experience taught me that our actions, no matter how small, can make a big difference in other people's lives. It has inspired me to seek out more opportunities to help and spread kindness wherever I go.

8. The moment I heard my name announced as the winner of the national essay competition, I felt an overwhelming sense of elation. I had spent weeks researching, writing, and revising my essay, often staying up late into the night. The hard work had paid off, and as I stood to receive my award, the applause of the audience filled me with joy and pride. This achievement was not just a personal victory but a confirmation of my passion for writing and storytelling.

9. My dream hangout spot would definitely have a huge, comfy sectional where all my friends and I can chill. We'd have string lights and lava lamps around to give off a cool vibe. There's a mini fridge loaded with our favorite snacks and a sound system for when we feel like having a dance-off. Big windows lead out to a balcony with hammocks and an awesome city view. This place is like our own little getaway where we can just be ourselves and have fun.

Lesson 15
Multiple-Choice

1. B
2. D
3. A
4. D
5. D

Fill-in-the-Blank

1. Extraneous
2. Fascinated
3. Fascinated
4. Lucid
5. Extraneous
6. Lucid

Lesson 17: Multiple-Choice

1. B
2. B
3. C
4. A
5. A

Fill-in-the-Blank

1. Euphemism
2. Implication
3. Harbinger
4. Endure
5. Disdain
6. Retaliate
7. Conscientious
8. Succumb

Definition and Synonym Match

Column A	Column B	Column C
1. Harbinger	C. A sign or warning that something, especially something momentous or calamitous, is likely to happen.	i. Precursor
2. Conscientious	H. Doing one's work diligently and thoroughly.	vi. Meticulous
3. Disdain	F. Scorn, contempt.	ii. Sneer
4. Implication	E. Something that is suggested or happens indirectly.	iii. Hint
5. Succumb	A. To give in to an overwhelming force or desire.	iv. Yield
6. Retaliate	G. To react to an attack by returning the same.	vii. Reprisal
7. Endure	D. To continue to exist in the same state; last.	v. Last
8. Euphemism	B. A mild or indirect word or expression substituted for one considered to be too harsh or blunt.	viii. Softening

Lesson 18
Multiple-Choice

1. C
2. A
3. C
4. B
5. B
6. D
7. D

Definition and Synonym Match

Match each word in Column A with its correct definition in Column B and its synonym in Column C.

Column A	Column B	Column C
1. Assimilate	D. To adapt or become similar to something.To weaken or reduce in strength.	iii. Absorb
2. Delineate	E. To outline or describe with precision.	vi. Define
3. Hypothesis	C. A suggested explanation for a phenomenon made as a starting point for further investigation.	iv. Theory
4. Debilitate	A. To weaken or reduce in strength.	i. Weaken
5. Furtive	G. Stealthy, secretive, or sneaky behavior.	ii. Stealthy
6. Haphazard	F. Lacking any obvious principle of organization.	vii. Random
7. Disseminate	B. To distribute or spread information widely.	v. Broadcast

Fill-in-the-Blank

1. disseminate
2. furtive
3. hypothesis
4. haphazard
5. assimilate
6. debilitated
7. delineate

Multiple-Choice #2

1. C
2. B
3. D
4. B
5. C
6. A
7. D

Lesson 19

1. C

2. The cat's behavior became erratic when **the new puppy was brought home because it felt threatened and unsettled by the unfamiliar presence in its territory.**

3. Due to his erratic sleep schedule, he **struggled to concentrate during morning classes and often found himself dozing off.**

4. The car's erratic movements alarmed the passengers because **it unpredictably swerved from lane to lane without warning.**

*ANSWERS MAY VARY

*

*

*

238

5. A

ANSWERS MAY VARY

6. After reviewing all the evidence presented in the debate, I finally had to concur that **the proposed environmental regulations would indeed benefit our community in the long run.**

_____ .

*

7. Although it was not my initial thought, I concur with the decision to **organize a charity** **organize a charity football match instead of a dance** _____ because **it will allow us to raise funds for new sports equipment.**

*

8. While I rarely concur with her opinions on movies, this time I agree that **the new movie** **about colonizing Mars excels with its impressive visual effects.** _____

_____ .

*

9. C

10. Despite feeling nervous, I stood up in class to denounce **the persistent bullying that** **was being overlooked by our school system** _____ .

*

11. In our society, we need to denounce behaviors like **discrimination and intolerance, which** **undermine the principles of equality and respect** _____ .

*

12. The whistleblower bravely denounced **the unethical practices within the corporation,** **exposing significant financial fraud that had gone unnoticed by the public and regulators** .

*

13. D

14. Implementing stricter consequences for littering can help deter **future instances of** **environmental disrespect and promote a cleaner community** _____ .

*

15. Adding more lighting in dark alleys is a method to deter **criminal activities,** **enhancing safety for residents and passersby in the area** _____ .

*

16. Installing security cameras around the school can deter **vandalism and bullying,** **creating a safer environment for all students** _____ .

*

17. A

239

18. The genesis of my interest in science began when __I attended my first astronomy camp__ **and saw the rings of Saturn through a telescope** .

19. Exploring the genesis of ancient civilizations helps us understand **how human societies** **have evolved over millennia and the factors that influenced their development** .

20. The genesis of the conflict can be traced back to __**deep-seated economic and social**__ **differences between the industrialized North and the agrarian South, leading to the Civil War** .

21. D

22. The argument presented by the politician was based on a fallacy because **it assumed** **economic growth automatically leads to improved social welfare** .

23. The belief that the earth is flat is a fallacy because **centuries of scientific research and** **astronomical observations have conclusively demonstrated that the earth is spherical.**

24. A historical fallacy in US history is the idea of "Manifest Destiny" because __it wrongly__ **believed that America had the right to expand westward without considering the harm it caused to Native American tribes.**

25. C

26. The depth of the ocean was so immense that I couldn't fathom __how creatures could__ **have evolved and lived without sunlight, surviving in such extreme and dark conditions.**

27. As I read about historical events, I found it hard to fathom __how so many women were__ **as witches in the 1600s and were executed without evidence, based only on mass hysteria.**

28. The idea of time travel is something I can't fathom because __it introduces too many__ **complications, such as changing the past or affecting the future in ways we can't predict.**

29. B

30. One idiosyncrasy of mine is ____ **to step over sidewalk cracks.**_____

_____.

31. Understanding the cultural idiosyncrasies of different countries can **help us communicate**
more effectively when we meet people from those places or visit them as tourists._____.

32. Despite his idiosyncrasies, he was respected for his _**dedication to volunteering and**_____
_**helping others in the community**_____.

Lesson 20
1. C
2. B
3. A
4. C
5. D
6. A
7. C
8. C

Word List and Definitions

A

Accessible: Easy to reach, enter, or understand.

Accurate: Correct, free from mistakes or errors.

Adversity: Difficulties or challenges; facing tough situations.

Advocate: Someone who publicly supports or recommends a particular cause or policy.

Aesthetic: Concerned with beauty or the appreciation of beauty.

Affiliation: The state of being officially attached or connected to an organization or group.

Alleviate: To make something less severe or more bearable.

Ambiguous: Having more than one possible meaning or interpretation; unclear.

Anatomy: The structure of an organism's body, including its organs and tissues.

Anecdote: A short and amusing or interesting story about a real incident or person.

Arbitrate: To act as an impartial judge in a dispute; to settle a disagreement.

Archaeologists: Scientists who study human history and prehistory through the excavation of artifacts and remains.

Artifacts: Objects made by humans, typically of cultural or historical significance, that are preserved for study or appreciation.

Assess: To evaluate or judge the quality, importance, or amount of something.

Assimilate: To take in and fully understand information or ideas.

Audacious: Showing a willingness to take bold risks, often in a daring or fearless manner.

Authenticate: To confirm or verify the validity or genuineness of something, usually through evidence or proof.

B

Bipedal: Walking or moving on two legs.

Bias: A preference or inclination for or against something, usually unfair and without rational justification.

C

Candid: Open, honest, and straightforward in speech or expression.

Censure: Strong disapproval or criticism, typically in a formal statement.

Chronological: Arranged in the order of time; according to the sequence of events.

Coalesce: To come together and form one mass or whole; to unite.

Coerce: To persuade or compel someone to do something through force or threats.

Cognizant: Aware or knowledgeable about something.

Collapse: A sudden and complete failure or breakdown; a falling together or inward.

Commensurate: Corresponding in size, degree, or extent; proportional.

Compromise: An agreement or settlement of a dispute that is reached by each side making concessions; to settle differences through mutual concessions.

Concealed: Hidden from view or kept secret; not easily detected or observed.

Concur: To agree or be of the same opinion.

Condemn: To express strong disapproval of; to denounce or criticize.

Conducive: Tending to produce a particular result or situation; favorable or advantageous.

Conscientious:

Constrain: To restrict or limit someone or something's freedom or action; to compel or force.

Constructive: Tending to build up or improve; positive and helpful in nature.

Context: The circumstances or setting in which an event occurs, which help to clarify its meaning or significance.

Contrive: To plan or devise something skillfully, typically with ingenuity or deception.

Convey: To communicate or make known a message, idea, or feeling; to transport or carry from one place to another.

Coordinated: Organized or planned to work together efficiently and harmoniously.

Correlate: To have a mutual relationship or connection, in which one thing affects or depends on another.

Criteria: Standards or rules used to judge or make decisions about something.

Crucial: Extremely important or essential for success.

Cumulative: Increasing or growing by accumulation or successive additions.

Cuneiform: Relating to the wedge-shaped characters used in ancient writing systems such as that of Mesopotamia.

Cynic: A person who believes that people are motivated purely by self-interest rather than acting for honorable or unselfish reasons.

D

Dearth: A scarcity or lack of something; an inadequate supply.

Debase: To reduce the quality, value, or character of something; to lower in rank, dignity, or significance.

Debilitate: To make (someone) weak or infirm; to hinder, delay, or weaken.

Decipher: To convert into understandable language; to interpret or decode.

Declamation: The act or art of speaking eloquently or passionately, often in public.

Decline: To become smaller, fewer, or less; to diminish or decrease in quantity, quality, or value.

Deductive: Relating to a method of reasoning in which specific conclusions are drawn from general principles or premises.

Delineate: To describe or portray (something) precisely; to outline or define with precision.

Denounce: To publicly declare to be wrong or evil; to condemn openly or formally.

Depict: To represent or show in the form of a picture or description; to portray or illustrate.

Deplore: To feel or express strong disapproval or regret for something, especially a behavior or action.

Desolate: Deserted or uninhabited, often referring to a place that feels bleak, empty, or lonely.

Deter: To discourage or prevent (someone) from doing something, typically by instilling doubt or fear of the consequences.

Devastate: To cause severe or widespread damage or destruction to something; to overwhelm with shock, grief, or sadness.

Deviate: To depart or stray from an established course or norm; to diverge or differ from the standard.

Dichotomy: A division or contrast between two things that are or are represented as being opposed or entirely different.

Differentiate: To recognize or express the difference between two or more things; to distinguish or discriminate.

Disdain: The feeling that someone or something is unworthy of one's consideration or respect; contempt or scorn.

Disparage: To speak of someone or something in a way that shows disrespect or lack of value; to belittle or criticize unfairly.

Dissenting: Holding or expressing opinions that are at variance with those commonly or officially held; differing or disagreeing.

E

Eccentric: Unconventional or slightly strange; departing from norms or conventions.

Efficacy: The ability to produce a desired or intended result; effectiveness.

Elation: A feeling of great joy, happiness, or exhilaration; a sense of intense excitement or jubilation.

Elucidate: To make something clear or easy to understand by explaining or clarifying it; to shed light on or illuminate.

Eminent: Famous and respected within a particular sphere or profession.

Empathy: The ability to understand and share the feelings, thoughts, or experiences of another person; the capacity for emotional identification or vicarious understanding.

Empirical: Based on or derived from observation, experience, or experiment rather than theory or speculation; verifiable through direct observation or experience.

Endure: To withstand or tolerate hardship, difficulty, or adversity; to bear or suffer patiently.

Enunciate: To pronounce words or sounds clearly and distinctly; to articulate or express with clarity and precision.

Ephemeral: Lasting for a very short time.

Equivocal: Ambiguous or open to more than one interpretation; deliberately vague or unclear in order to deceive or mislead.

Erratic: Irregular, unpredictable, or inconsistent in movement, behavior, or quality; deviating from the usual or expected course.

Escalate: To increase rapidly in intensity, extent, or magnitude; to become or make something more severe or serious.

Euphemism: A mild or indirect word or expression used in place of a more direct or harsh one to avoid offense or unpleasantness.

Exacerbate: To make a problem, situation, or condition worse or more severe; to aggravate or intensify.

Excerpt: A short extract or passage taken from a larger work, document, or piece of writing; a selection or portion of text.

Exhausted: Extremely tired or fatigued; completely drained of energy or strength; thoroughly depleted or used up.

Exhaustive: Thorough and comprehensive; covering all possible details, aspects, or considerations; complete and exhaustive.

Exhilarate: To make someone feel very happy, animated, or invigorated; to fill with high spirits, energy, or enthusiasm.

Exonerate: To absolve or clear someone of blame, guilt, or responsibility; to declare innocent or free from accusation.

Explicit: Fully and clearly expressed or demonstrated; leaving nothing implied or unstated; definite or unambiguous in meaning or intention.

Exploit: To make full use of and derive benefit from (a resource).

Exposition: A comprehensive explanation or setting forth of meaning or intent.

Extinction: The complete disappearance or eradication of a species from the Earth.

Extraneous: Irrelevant or unrelated to the subject being dealt with.

Extremism: The holding of extreme political or religious views.

F

Fallacy: A mistaken belief, especially one based on unsound argumentation.

Falter: to hesitate or waver in action, belief, or purpose.

Fascinated: Captivated or intensely interested in something; absorbed by a subject, idea, or activity.

Fathom: To understand or comprehend the depth or meaning of something; to grasp or measure the extent or intensity of something.

Feign: To pretend or simulate; to fake or fabricate an appearance or emotion in order to deceive or mislead others.

Foreseeable: able to be anticipated or predicted with a reasonable degree of certainty.

Foreshadow: To indicate or suggest something, especially a future event, beforehand; to give a warning or hint of what is to come.

Formidable: Inspiring fear, respect, or awe due to size, strength, difficulty, or complexity; daunting or intimidating in nature.

Fossils: The preserved remains or traces of ancient organisms, such as bones, shells, or imprints, found in sedimentary rock layers.

Formulate: to create or develop a plan, strategy, or idea systematically and methodically.

Fortify: To strengthen or reinforce something, especially defenses or structures; to make something more secure or resistant to attack.

Fossils: The remains or impression of a prehistoric organism preserved in petrified form or as a mold or cast in rock.

Furtive: Done or acting in a secretive, sly, or stealthy manner; characterized by stealth or secrecy in order to avoid attention or detection.

G

Genesis: The origin, beginning, or creation of something; the starting point or initial stage of a process or development.

Germane: Relevant or closely related to the topic or subject at hand; pertinent or applicable to the matter being discussed or considered.

Gregarious: Sociable, outgoing, or fond of the company of others; enjoying or seeking the companionship of a group or community.

Guile: Cunning, deceitfulness, or craftiness in behavior or speech; the use of clever or dishonest tactics to achieve one's goals or deceive others.

H

Hackneyed: Used so often as to lack freshness or originality; overused to the point of becoming trite or cliché.

Haphazard: Lacking any obvious principle of organization or planning; random or chaotic.

Harbinger: Something that foreshadows or predicts future events; an indicator or sign of what is to come, often used in a negative sense.

Hieroglyphics: A system of writing using pictures or symbols, especially associated with ancient Egypt; a method of communication using characters that represent objects or concepts.

Hypothesis: A proposed explanation for a phenomenon or a scientific problem that can be tested through experimentation or observation.

Hypothetical: Based on assumptions or conjecture rather than actual observation or evidence; imagined or supposed rather than proven or factual.

I

Idiosyncrasy: A characteristic, habit, or mannerism that is unique to an individual; a distinctive or peculiar feature that sets someone apart.

Implication: Something that is suggested or indirectly conveyed rather than explicitly stated.

Incoherent: Lacking clarity or logical connection; not expressed or organized in a clear or understandable manner; disjointed or confusing.

Infuriate: To make someone extremely angry or enraged; to provoke intense irritation or exasperation in someone.

Intercede: To intervene or mediate in a dispute or conflict on behalf of another person; to act as an intermediary in order to reconcile differences or negotiate a resolution.

J

Judicious: Showing good judgment or careful consideration when making decisions or taking action.

L

Loquacious: Tending to talk a lot

Lucid: Clear and easily understood; rational and mentally sound.

Lyrical: Expressing the writer's emotions in an imaginative and beautiful way, especially in poetry.

M

Magnitude: The great size, extent, or importance of something.

Mediate: To intervene or help settle differences between conflicting parties.

P

Palpable: Able to be touched or felt; tangible.

Perpetrate: To commit or carry out (a harmful, illegal, or immoral act), typically a crime or wrongdoing.

Pivotal: Of crucial importance or significance, often marking a turning point.

Prevalent: Widespread or commonly occurring; existing or happening often.

Profound: Having deep insight or understanding; intellectually deep or penetrating.

Pseudonym: A fictitious name, especially one used by an author instead of their real name.

R

Rationale: The underlying reason or justification for a decision, action, or belief; the logic or reasoning behind something.

Reconcile: To restore friendly relations between; to make consistent or compatible.

Reliable: Able to be trusted or depended on consistently.

Resilience: The ability to recover quickly from difficulties; toughness.

Retaliate: To make an attack or assault in return for a similar attack.

Rigorous: Characterized by thoroughness and strict adherence to standards, often involving intense effort and attention to detail.

Roam: To move about or travel without a specific destination.

S

Sabotage: Deliberate destruction or disruption of something, especially for a specific purpose or goal.

Severely: In a manner that is very serious or harsh; to a great degree.

Spurred: To encourage or prompt something to happen, often by providing motivation or stimulation.

Squander: To waste (something, especially money or resources) in a reckless or foolish manner.

Stylus: A small, pointed instrument used for writing, drawing, or engraving, typically held in the hand.

Succumb: To yield to superior strength or force; to give in to pressure or temptation.

T

Tirade: A long, angry speech or criticism, typically one that is filled with harsh language.

U

Ubiquity: The state of being everywhere, or seeming to be everywhere, at the same time.

V

Verdant: Green with vegetation; covered in green plants or grass.

Vexation: The state of being annoyed, frustrated, or worried, typically as a result of something unexpected or problematic.

Vulnerabilities: Weaknesses or gaps in something that can be exploited or harmed, especially in systems or security measures.

Also by Natasha Attard, Ph.D.

The Spelling Practice Workbook 6th Grade

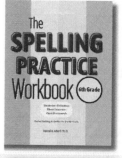

The Spelling Practice Workbook 7th Grade: Guided Activities to Increase your Word Power. Consolidates and Complements Homeschooling of the English Language
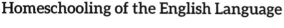

The Spelling Practice Workbook 8th Grade: Guided Activities to Increase your Word Power. Consolidates and Complements Homeschooling of the English Language

Vocabulary and Spelling Practice 7th Grade: Intensive Practice Workbook and Guided Activities to Increase Your Word Power.

Vocabulary Building 7th Grade Workbook: Guided Activities to Increase your Word Power. Consolidates and Complements Homeschooling of the English Language

Made in United States
Orlando, FL
21 August 2024

50625453R00139